IMOGEN THE DREAMER

STEVE WILKES

Copyright 2012 by Steve Wilkes

Published by My Spirit Books 2012

The right of Steve Wilkes to be identified as the Author of the Work
has been asserted by him in accordance with the Copyright, Designs
and Patents Act 1988.

First published in Great Britain in 2012 by My Spirit Books,
Maidstone TV Studio, Vinters Park,
Maidstone, Kent ME14 5NZ
www.myspiritbooks.com

Cover Design by Lee Carnwell
Editor & Layout by Kim Farnell
Publishing Director Adam Fronteras

Printed and bound in the UK by Biddles, part of the MPG Books
Group, Bodmin and King's Lynn

British Library Cataloguing-in-Publication Data
A catalogue record for this book is available on request from the
British Library

ISBN 978-1-908810-021

DEDICATION

THIS BOOK IS DEDICATED TO CHUNG FU,
DANARAY, SALLY, SOFIE, ARAURA, MICHELLE,
SUZI, DORI, LESLIE AND ALL OF OUR BLESSED
SPIRIT GUIDES

THANK YOU FOR THE JOURNEY WE HAVE SHARED
TOGETHER IN OUR DEVELOPMENT OVER THE
FOUR YEARS

ACKNOWLEDGEMENTS

I would like to thank the following people in helping to get this book into production: My Spirit Productions - Adam Fronteras, Michele Knight and Kim Farnell.

And I am grateful to the following people for ordering advance copies:

Walter Aerts
Angelee Agarwal
Asymptotix Ltd
Frida Backman
Emma Bagnall
Jenny Barnette
Douglas Buckingham
Sally Bull
Andrew Cooper
Tiffany Crosara
Angela Cuthbert
Gowsia Hyder
Odette Kurland
MSG Pennefeather
Josette Pouilloux
Lyn Houston
Sharlea Johnson
Fadila Kerrad
Vashti Seymour
Keith Smith
Canan Uras

IMOGEN THE DREAMER

AN INTRODUCTORY SPIRITUAL PSYCHIC DEVELOPMENT COURSE

STEVE WILKES AND DANARAY

PREFACE

NAOMI OZANIEC

THE MAGICAL STORY has a long and respectable history; its strength lies in the unique power of the imagination to stir the mind. Dion Fortune knew this secret well and employed it to good effect in her tales of magic, karmic resolution and personal empowerment. Stever Wilkes is a new writer in the tradition of waking the magical imagination so that the reader can become a participant in a different reality.

Works of the imagination should never be underestimated; far from being, "unreal", imaginative fiction can become solid fact – for instance, *The Mists of Avalon*[1] has been read as a blueprint for inspired action.

Steve has chosen to set personal exercises against a fictional-imaginative background. I am surprised to see this not done more often since it provides a necessary balance between study and personal realisation. After all, the

1 Mists of Avalon, Marion Zimmer Bradley, 1983.

i

shamanic student must learn to discern the significance of inner imaginative fiction set against the more solid external experience of the senses. Steve writes, "The imagination itself is the gateway to spirit, so the juxtaposition of the two modes of mind is perfectly justified. Beyond shamanic work descriptive narrative is also used to set the scene in group ceremonial magical workings when it is called "the composition of place". Once again, the imagination precedes and prepares the way for magical work.

The Songs of Danaray is a series of three books: *Imogen the Dreamer*; *Jessica the Oracle* and *Bereklem the King and the Land.* However, Steve's tale tells a very personal story since it is also a record of three different lives in which Steve has worked closely with his primary guide, Danary, and he includes Danary as a co-author of the current work. The book is also more than a story to feed the imagination – it is a practical journey to awaken the soul-powers. But all students of the magical mind should understand that healing journeys are invariably passages of breaking and remaking. Steve knows this only too well and he makes this very clear.

Steve's practical experience as a shamanic practitioner is impressive. He has successfully effected distant healings and exorcisms and has taught in Buenos Ares, Turkey, Spain and New Zealand among other far flung places. He has worked as a professional reader and estimates that to date he has given more than 35,000 readings! There is no doubt that Steve is, as they say, "the real deal".

Steve's earlier career as a mental health practitioner has given him a unique and solid grounding in the many ills that afflict the human mind and soul. His natural desire to heal such wounds has led him from a traditional psychiatric model to an immersion into shamanic spirituality. These two modes are never separated and Steve brings a deep and compassionate heart to the curriculum he has created under the auspices of Danary, his lives-long teacher, gatekeeper and twin soul.

Steve is also one of the pagan priests to have emerged through the newly birthed Avalon tradition which is perhaps better known for its goddess focus. New "traditions" must expect to be questioned; Avalon uses its own ceremonial correspondences, and indeed has invested the name of Nolava with the qualities of the feminine divine. This invention-creation-realisation may annoy some, but as a practitioner of the system, Steve simply says, "Well it works," and that is proof enough of some power inherent in the land of Glastonbury. As a point of history, divinities have been brought into being, often for political reasons. Love it or hate it, Avalon has captured enough imaginations to become a psychic reality and Steve Wilkes is proud to be among its first initiates, practitioners and priests. If you decide to journey with Steve you are most certainly in safe hands.

Steve's journey does not stand still and he has apprenticed himself to older magical systems beyond the primarily devotional Avalonian path; it is always good to know that the teacher is also a student so that the creative well of inspiration and understanding never runs dry. Steve is also attuned to the evolutionary Aquarian times in which we live and sees himself as a weaver of traditions both old and new. Such eclecticism was once meaningless, but today when the treasure house of all traditions stand open, fusion and cross-fertilisation are inevitable and humanity must take what it needs to create a purposeful future. Steve is now working in Spain to help build a priesthood of skilled practitioners, both men and women, who are committed to an evolutionary spirituality. He speaks of interesting work with the indigenous deities of Iberia, so watch out for an emerging stream of cultural infusion far away from Avalon.

Steve offers a comprehensive and sensible structure to the vast world of psychic development in a shamanic framework. Not surprisingly the work begins by establishing the personal relationship with inner spirit guides who maintain a central role in the life and experience of the student. The course includes practical experiences in psychicism, clairvoyance, mediumship, shamanic journeying and connection with power animals, the ancestors and elemental powers. I undertook several of the exercises myself with good and lasting results. Steve has placed his solid experience at your service in this book; I can guarantee it won't be his last.

INTRODUCTION

*T*HE *SONGS OF DANARAY* is a series of three books: *Imogen the Dreamer, Jessica the Oracle* and *Bereklem the King and the Land*. These books I feel offer a unique expression, for they record both three different lives that Danaray (my primary spirit guide) and I have lived together in our incarnated history and the content of the spiritual development courses that we teach and have taught together.

The story of *Imogen the Dreamer* weaves through each chapter of this book, I have deliberately combined fiction and subjective, experiential spirituality as Danaray and I felt that part of the difficulty students face with their spirituality is in relation to their concepts of reality – what they believe to be the truth and what they believe they might have imagined. In our understanding, the imagination is the gateway to spirit; it is the place where we weave our connection with other levels of reality.

A number of years ago I experienced a vision when I was

journeying in the spirit worlds where I saw a huge vertical block of white light and knew from a place of spiritual knowing that this light symbolised my soul. Within this white light I saw my soul expressing itself as an amoeba. Just above that, I saw my soul as a plant and then as a tree, and then as different animals followed by numerous humans moving up the pillar of light, rather than horizontally through linear time. The top of the pillar of light opened out into the everything, the great expression of the divine. What particularly struck me about this vision was that everything was happening at the same time. Past, present and future were all now and everything that I did or thought as Steve affected everything that happened in all of my soul lives. The beauty of it however was that whatever happened in that pillar of light, that Jacob's ladder, the expression of the pillar as a whole was always the divine.

Chapter One of this book explores the connection with spirit guides and puts the relationship with these guides at the centre of the spiritual development process. Danary and I use hypnotherapeutic techniques, sound and imagination to link with the students' guides and start a conscious relationship. We then teach the students, working in pairs, to journey to their partner's spirit guides for information and healing. While in pairs students learn the techniques of psychometry and are often able to perform their first clairvoyant readings for each other. The class starts with invocation of Spirit and ends with thanks to Spirit. Powerful grounding and centring techniques are taught throughout the course and the book.

Gatekeepers change as we spiritually evolve, as our lives weave into the greater experience of who we are, the sublime expression of who we can be. Danaray, my twin soul, assumed the role of my gatekeeper in my temporal experience of late 2004. My experience of her role is that she is responsible for which or what energies enter into my auric bodies, or which beings I connect with clairvoyantly or mediumistically. Danaray currently plays a major role in the organisation of my spiritual experience in this incarnation.

When we discuss the spirit world(s) or our experience of divinity, terminology can become ambiguous. Time, for example, is not a function of divinity when it expresses itself as the all, but is an expression of the experience of physicality and duality. Hence, when I express that Danaray became my gatekeeper in 2004, I am using a convention of human physical experience. The truth is that from Danaray's perspective, that moment of now (or late 2004) has always been present. I will discuss the concept of time in greater detail when we look at journeys of past and future lives.

There are two spirit beings, two guides, whom I experience as my primary influences. Chung Fu, or Old Chinese as he sometimes calls himself, is an advanced being, a teacher guide who helps humans and spirit guides to connect with each other. Chung Fu has been dead for over a thousand years and appears both clairvoyantly and when channelling through a human host (referred to by Spirit as a vehicle) as an ancient Tibetan monk. Chung Fu tells me that he has been channelling through human bodies for seven hundred years and that our bodies have changed quite a bit over time.

Danaray manifests in one of three different lives in this series of books, two female, one male, all from Anglesey in North Wales. Firstly, as Jessica, an oracle witch magician in the late fourteenth century. Secondly, as Imogen, a druidic shamanic dreamer defending the sacred lands from Roman domination and finally as Bereklem, a pre-historical tribal king, from the time when the land and the king were as one.

Chung Fu calls himself an honorary spirit guide and, although we work together closely on a daily basis, he has a more eclectic, universal role. Danaray is my gatekeeper and the other half of my soul. Our work creates a loving partnership. At one point we were considering incarnating together, but decided on this occasion to have one of us work in the physical, the other in the ethereal. It is as recognition of her teachings that I am writing these books.

Chapter Two introduces the student to shamanic–like journeying by taking them with their spirit guides to the lower worlds to meet their power animals (the primal spirits that work with the shaman)and map their worlds. Students again work in pairs and visit each other's lower worlds and power animals for spiritual development messages and healings. Students are introduced to the seven major chakras and a form of psychic reading that focuses their intention and breath on their partner's chakras.

Much of our work is shamanic in nature. The experience of journeying in the spirit worlds is both transformative and ecstatic; it underlines so much of whom I am and the way that I intuitively know how to work in the spiritual realms. My work in this life started relatively organically when others approached me asking if I would teach them based on the way I work.

I have had many lives working as a shaman. In one of my lives working with Danaray, my primary sense was olfactory, and as a little boy I could literally "sniff out" someone coming for miles. This ability later translated into "sniffing out" spiritual information from the shamanic worlds.

In my current life, the memory of shamanic experience came primarily in my thirties. I began to work with Running Wolf, a shamanic teacher and spirit guide who reminded me experientially of the composition of the spirit worlds and took me through a number of initiatory experiences. In other lives I have experienced, Running Wolf had been my shamanic teacher and mentor and hence working with him felt very natural. In my current life, my shamanic initiatory experiences started at birth – part of shamanic initiation is to go through the death experience and I was born "blue" and near death. This was always meant to be.

Shamanic journeying is taught throughout my introductory classes, and daily shamanic journeys to various ancient pantheons characterise the advanced course. The beauty of the daily shamanic journeys, mantras, mudras and ceremonies is in the reports from students of their pragmatic, grounded, mundane sense of increased psychicness, the opening of the senses experienced through daily connection with spirit and divinity.

Chapter Three introduces the student to the higher world (the heavens); it takes them to meet their shamanic "wise one" for healing and connection and leads them to paradise and a connection with the aspects of divinity that work for them. On these journeys, they work with their power animals and their spirit guides, strengthening those relationships and often connecting with angels. The students journey in pairs to each meet the "wise one" of the other for healing and developmental messages. We teach a form of auric reading which involves the spinning of certain chakras.

The introductory course explores the three different shamanic worlds – the lower, middle and higher worlds common to shamanic experiences across culture and history.

It introduces shamanic techniques for meeting spirit guides and fosters relationships with power animals. It additionally teaches the student to journey in the spirit worlds of others, noticing similarities and vast differences of another person's worlds compared to one's own. Shamanism in this context is about freedom; freedom to connect to spirit and journey through the universe in any time and place. Working shamanically, I teach students to build the seven point sacred circle in the meadows between the worlds and later to transfer this model and extend it to perform ritual in this world.

Danaray and I have no desire or intention to convert you the reader, or you the student, to anything. We do not choose for you to walk any particular path or adhere to any particular dogma. We are happy to work with you if you work with the goddess, the Christ, the Buddha or Allah, or indeed experience the divine as the universe. We do not want you to walk our path for it is ours. We are, however, more than happy to share anything with you to aid you on your path. Similarly, we work with particular tools as these tools work well for us. If you attend our classes, we ask you to work with these particular tools while in class. After the course, you are free to use or discard the tools at will.

The introductory course takes you on a journey so that you can begin to see what is possible. It gives you a taste of direct contact with Spirit. The process of working with Spirit is experiential; there is no attempt to prove anything to you. The journey with Spirit is about establishing a relationship, not satisfying external societal models. The key here is the utilization of the most powerful creative tool that you have, your imagination, for that is what our journey with Spirit is about – creation! We are constantly incarnating and manifesting the ethereal through our bodies into the physical. We are increasing the experience of all that there is (the divine spirit) through ourselves. We are not separate from Spirit; we are Spirit in the process of incarnation. We are part of that divine spirit, the all, experiencing itself as us. When Danaray and teach, we prompt you to remember, we encourage you to know, because you entirely trust your connection to the larger part of yourself that is Spirit. One of my teachers Kathy Jones says, "Trust everything you get and don't be afraid to be wrong". This epitomises the nature of the reality you create at any time.

The process of working with the imagination is the process of tapping into that river of creativity that we call Spirit, the divine, the creatrix. So often we search for some external truth, some illusory thoughtform to prove something to self, by which we usually mean prove something to others. Working with Spirit in whatever form, as aspects of the divine, spirit guides, angels, elementals, ancestors etc. is an ability of, an option for, all human beings. In effect, working with Spirit is not an option, but is something that is impossible not to do. The only choice here is whether we work with Spirit consciously or unconsciously. Seeing ourselves as mere skin encapsulated beings and nothing beyond is only one limited level of perception. Of course, the drama of the outside world and our separation from it is true at one level, the level of Malkuth, but only at that one limited level.

The healing of our personal relationship with our relationship to external reality starts with Spirit and our imagining of Spirit in our imagination. What is potentially being offered is a journey that completely transforms your life and your experience of reality. The reason that it is a potential offer is that the effectiveness of the offer relies on whether you choose now to begin to experience All That Is consciously or not.

Chapter Six describes students' journeys in the middle world to the Temple of Avalon for healing with energy and sound and to connect with the Lady of Avalon. They then experience journeys to Isis, the Christ, the Buddha, Allah and a medicine woman who sings in the new day. The middle world is the most challenging of the worlds and we teach about it later in the course when strong relationships with spirit guides and power animals have begun. The techniques taught to enter the middle worlds include journeying through your own or another person's chakras. Straight clairvoyant readings working directly with your own spirit guides are also taught at this stage.

Spirit works through the emotional body. Clairvoyants and psychics are called "sensitives" for a very good reason; we feel things before we know them through other senses. Many people when they start working with Spirit consciously go into crisis as buried emotional material comes to the surface of their consciousness and manifests in their reality for the purposes of healing. Buried emotional material is often related to childhood and the process of repressing childhood's dreams as something that many in society often consider to be not real, and reject as just childhood fantasy. This childhood fantasy is the faculty of imagination itself, the raw creative power of unmanifest spirit, the idea often referred to as the inner child.

We teach in a circle, not as teachers at the front of a class, but as leading participants. The circle is a symbol of the whole, a microcosm of the All. The experience of being in circle is also transformational: each person reflects to you in a very direct way all that your journey is about and each person acts as a mirror for everyone else in the circle. Often, these collective experiences bring up karmic memories and past life connections realised between participants. The amazing web weaved by Spirit means that exactly the right people are bought together to heal, balance and grow.

The mirror itself is a transformative device. In the morning when we look in the mirror we see ourselves exactly how we are or who we are. However, the being we are looking at in the mirror is not us, it is an-other, for we are the being observing the being in the mirror. The being we observe in the mirror is therefore both who or what we are and who or what we are not. This is true generally of all of our relationships. We see who we are, or who we no longer are, by virtue of whom we are not and these experiences are often exacerbated or increased in circle. Spirit demonstrates time and again how it manifests our reality through other people, and how amazing the spiritual matrix is that brings exactly the right people together at the right time.

I trained and initiated as a pagan priest, as a priest of Avalon, with my spirit guides, power animals and other spirit beings, and much of my teaching has that flavour. I work with a wheel of life called the Wheel of Brigitana named after two powerful ancestral goddesses of Britain (Brigit and Ana). The wheel differs in a number of ways from elemental wheels of Wicca, ceremonial magic etc. The Wheel of Brigitana is goddess specific, although here and there a god is implied – for example, Nodens, god of the sea is the son of Domnu, goddess of water, and the lover of the lover goddess. The debate about the place of the god in a matrifocal system is current and ongoing, a debate that I am intensely involved in and actively developing. The Wheel of Brigitana is an amazing structure that has many layers of experience integrated within it. Brigitana celebrates the eight pagan festivals of the Sun, the Sabbats – Imbolc, Ostara, Beltane, Litha, Lammas, Mabon, Samhain and Yule. It also honours a ninth holding place in the centre of the wheel which is the All.

The Wheel of Brigitana was intuited by Kathy Jones as part of a working ceremony and through walking the sacred land of Avalon. Its relationship between the elements and their directions differs from that of the Wiccan (and other) wheels. For example, with Brigitana air is in the north, while with the Wiccan wheel earth is in the north. I don't feel either is wrong; both clearly work and I use both at different times. Brigitana however is audacious; it trusts intuition, place and experience over tradition and it also breaks new ground as a reflection of a new tradition, that of Nolava, Goddess of Avalon.

The process of invoking a Wiccan/witch wheel involves calling to the elemental watchtowers from the four primary directions: north, east, south and west. The watchtowers are powerful astral magical places, places of initiatory depth for the magician. The ceremonialist creates a space between the worlds and seals it by walking the circle three times deosil. The circle is then viewed, and experienced as sacred space for magical purposes, and the goddess and the god are invited in. Sometimes, particular deities are named and at other times a generic goddess or god is invoked.

The energetic experience of invoking the Wheel of Brigitana is entirely different. Nine places (rather than five) are evoked (and then often invoked) in ritual ceremonial prayer. Specific goddesses, elemental priestesses peculiar to Avalon (the Morgens), power animals, plants and trees typify this magical energy. Sound and poetry are used, weaving the energy for the priestess' or ceremonialist's experience and the experience of others present. Rather than energetically seal a sacred circle, the ceremonialist activates their imagination and sees or feels the divine beings coming towards them, creating the sacred space that way. The ceremonialist uses breath to breathe divine energy into their body for the purposes of personal transformation, and invites others to join this experience, after which they exhale to create sacred space.

The Wheel of Brigitana is a healing manifestation wheel. Air in the north is seen/felt as Spirit (whereas the Wiccan wheel uses fire in the south). The energy moves sunwise to the east and the fire of the mind. Focus, courage and desire manifest at the level of thought. The energy moves sunwise to the south, to the place of water, the experience of emotion and the feeling of manifestation. The energy moves west to the place of Earth, physicality, the goddess Gaia who manifests all of our dreams and the implication of the Green Man who protects our creations. The movement from spirit (air) to physicality (earth) is extraordinarily powerful when weaving divine energy.

The cross quarters: Imbolc, Beltane, Lammas and Samhain (north-east, south-east, south-west and north-west respectively) represent the cycle of life of the feminine divine: the maiden, the lover, the pregnant mother and the crone. Each of them has tools which are very powerful ceremonial accessories of manifestation. The quarters, cross quarters and centre of the Wheel of Brigitana have animals attached to them in direct relation to the time of year, the particular elemental divine energy and British mythology.

Terminology and definition, belief structures and ideology become complicated when working with or teaching clairvoyance and mediumship, and hence require some comment. At times I work with them in very different ways or for very different reasons, than do other spiritual traditions. Spiritualists, when defining their work, often refer to mediumship as connecting to recent ancestors of the person they are reading for, working with spirit guides is not usually part of that definition. Strictly speaking, the medium is the bridge between the spirit worlds and the world of physicality. I, like spiritualists, describe mediumship as the practice of making direct contact with recognisable ancestors who are in spirit. Clairvoyance, clairaudience and clairsentience literally mean "clear seeing", "clear hearing" and "clear feeling". However, I (and others) refer to these terms in relationship to my spirit guide work as a way of distinguishing that work from the mediumship work defined above. I have a great respect for spiritualism and have learned a great deal from different spiritualist teachers both in the UK and in New Zealand. However, more and more my ethos has begun to differ from theirs. As a pagan priest dedicated to the service of the Lady of Avalon, the ancient goddess of the Paradise Isle of the Dead in the English West Country, working with their semi-Christian Jehovah based spirituality became gradually more untenable for me. There are further differences in the expression of my spirituality. Spiritualists see the work with recent ancestors as the highest form of spiritual work. That is, I think, because the narrative of spiritualism is to seek proof of life beyond the grave and hence demonstrating connection to someone recognisable that has died becomes the point.

For me, the relationship to ancestors on my spiritual path takes an entirely different form. I have absolutely no interest in proving continued existence to anyone else, for each soul must walk their own path of experience and growth. Indeed, I am only aware of working with recent ancestors for two reasons: Firstly, to help the individual experiencing grief issues relating to the death of someone close who has come for a reading(demonstrating proof here is helpful to my client). Secondly, teaching students with particular leanings towards mediumship on their own paths. Mediumship seems to delight some students and repel others. Teaching mediumship in Turkey proved very interesting as many students found mediumship challenging for cultural or religious reasons. This chapter also describes how to work with shamanic techniques for purposes of manifestation and identifying your life/soul path.

Working with ancestors for me has entirely different connotations to the Spiritualist norm of proving life after death. Spiritually and psychically tracing the energies and karma of our ancestral lines moves us towards holism and nearer the great divine source, the All. On many levels, my ancestors (their experiences, beliefs, memories relationship with spirit, magic, health and DNA) define who I am now. I have incarnated into these bloodlines in order to experience challenges related specifically to them. I am also aware of having incarnated into these bloodlines before, for my past lives have crossed through these ancestral lines on a number of occasions. I am the reincarnation of my own great grandparent[s].

So why work with ancestors at all? I sense that all life is about growth, about ourselves as a part of the divine experiencing being the divine. In this way, growth and holism are therefore, in a tautological sense, healing. Life experienced in the spirit worlds is still about soul development, and as our ancestors continue to grow in the spirit worlds they more and more take responsibility for what they have created. In a physical, biological sense we are the consequences of the karma accrued, the creation of our ancestors. In a collective sense, we were born into an environment created by our ancestors. This understanding is not a statement that denies personal responsibility for my reality, for indeed I have often been my own ancestor and hence am healing my own karma. It is however a recognition of a model of perception of collective, universal spiritual growth, for my ancestors are both in the spirit worlds and alive in me and others simultaneously.

The Native American and Tibetan traditions of spirituality work with grandmother and grandfather energies and the divine as a universal whole. As a pagan priest, I work with the goddess and god who are in effect my ancient ancestors and primal expressions of the source, the creatix of the night and day, touching the place of All that there is. The connection to the divine then is an expression of who I truly am, for there is no part of me that isn't divine, for that energy of life, of my ancestors, of spirit, courses through my blood vessels as a unique expression of the divine, the All. The divine, the All, the goddess and the god and my ancestors are also manifest as expressions of Mother Earth, (for if we are not made of her energy what are we made of?) and hence in this way the trees, the mountains, the oceans and the animals are my ancestors, my brothers and my sisters and various expressions of me.

Chapter Four teaches students how to build sacred circles in the inner worlds (or to be precise in the meadow between the worlds) by using the seven directions: north, east, south, west, down, up and self. The first four directions use the power animals on the Wheel of Brigitana and the other directions invite personal power animals, spirit guides, angels and divinity into the sacred circle built by evoking the four directions. The student learns to use their own body as a portal to the other worlds and work with the axis mundi or world tree at the centre of the universe. The shamanic worlds are not only vertical in arrangement; they also work on the horizontal axis to move backwards and forwards through time. In this class, students journey through their own DNA to their souls and the circles of their past, parallel and future lives for information and healing. Also in this class, the student learns a clairvoyant technique that involves focusing on their partner's chakras.

I experience another line of soul development which expresses itself through past and future lives. I am describing here a model of understanding rather than perhaps a literal truth. My experience of spirit is that we live many human (and other) lives in the journey of our souls. What I am attempting to convey here is that the universe is so incredible that my model of truth is only one, yet an incredibly valid part of the kaleidoscope of truth/reality. As I express this process, I am stating the experience of my evolution through time, through many lives with the same beings, the same souls. These beings make up layers of soul family that all evolve at different levels because of their soul relationships with each other. Although it is true that at an ultimate level we are all one family (or to be precise all one being), in terms of less ultimate comprehension the narrative structure of layers of soul family works for me. The beings in my soul family have known me since the beginning of time, for all time, since the no-thing became the everything.

Within my soul family, there are beings at various levels of spiritual evolution. However, the evolutionary experience is symbiotic for all of us – I evolve because they do; they evolve because I do. Within the inner layers of my soul family, I am aware of beings with whom I have incarnated into many lives. We have had every kind of relationship with each other – lovers, siblings, parents, children etc. In the experience of Steve in this current life I am exploring, I am aware of numbers of my soul family with whom I have incarnated. I call them soul mates, and the others who work with me in spirit I call my spirit guides. One of the major reasons that I primarily work with spirit guides as opposed to recent ancestors is that it is my experience that guides are generally much more evolved. There are some that state that we only have one spirit guide, to me this is semantics. Whether you believe that we have many guides or just one is irrelevant in terms of working with Spirit in practical terms. I have thirty-four spirit beings working with me at present, including my shamanic power and totem animals. These are beings that I love and know well and work with on a daily basis.

I experience in our time an unfolding of spiritual awareness, a deeper exploration of the inner worlds and a seeking of new meaning where philosophy, ideology and religion all fail. Connection with Spirit, with an ancient wisdom-based knowledge, broadens the individual's experience of reality and brings about deep healing at all levels. However, the process of spirit, this wisdom that is beyond the mind, can challenge psychology, create existential predicament and shake up deep beliefs about self through encounters with alternative realities, for in reality spiritual development training is not a nice gentle process, but is a powerful transformative journey designed to spark the process of personal and collective healing.

Spiritual life is never really separate from the rest of life. Through spiritual awareness, you experience that the spirit world(s) interpenetrates all spheres of existence.

Connection with Spirit (in whatever form that is right for the individual) is more than just an expression of belief or an externalised ritual as is typical within Christianity and other modern expressions of monotheistic patriarchal religions. It is an intense inner experience of personal transformation and a process of revealing the extraordinary possibilities of personal and collective human consciousness. Reaching the source, or going deeper into the Earth, or deeper into self, we remember a more archaic level of human experience, the primal power animals, the elementals and the aspects of ancient divinity.

Working with your spiritual development is not solely an intellectual process as is beloved by science and humanism. You cannot study it from books alone and remain at an objective analytical distance. It doesn't adhere to the cry of rationalism that the only way to reach the truth is by constantly using cynicism until all attempts at disproving Spirit has failed. This belief is so central to Western thinking: *Do not trust the internal, the feminine, the subjective, for only through rationalism and the perceived norm, material external reality can any truth be reached.* Spiritual development goes deeper, much deeper, and interfaces between your consciousness and the spiritual sphere. Only through an existential and experiential relationship with Spirit can we truly understand the nature of our individual life paths and the enormity of the divine.

For there is something about the experience of Spirit that is central to knowing about Spirit, understanding that the spiritual cannot be reduced to ordinary reality, historical or cultural, social or political factors alone, but that the spiritual transcends all and is the essence of all of those things manifest and unmanifest, experienced and yet to be experienced. Scepticism about your experience of the spiritual in and of itself cannot lead you to the place of knowing.

Henri Corbin[2] refers to what he calls an *agnostic reflex,* which has a kind of academic respectability and has the effect of paralysing the mind, closing it off from the dimension of experience. I see the *agnostic reflex* as an inherited belief or a response to an inherited belief. However, belief itself is not fixed. It is a tool for shaping our realities. Often our beliefs are inherited. They belong to the morass of ideological norms present in the collective unconsciousness. They are inherited in childhood from influential others: society, family, educational institutions etc. and even our justifications for those beliefs come from a pool of collective unconsciousness. Much of the time these beliefs are not questioned and are taken as fixed.

However, not all beliefs serve the individual, particularly those that undermine self–esteem or deny the validity of whole areas of knowledge and consciousness such as supra–consciousness or subjectivity. Fixing beliefs of choice (i.e. those beliefs one would choose to aid growth), and adhering to them whatever the experience of external reality may be present in one's consciousness, alters the experience of your reality and hence changes that place of knowing and/or feeling. Reality itself is holographic and forms around the beliefs, emotions, thoughts, behaviour and utterances of the individual and the collective.

The holographic nature of the universe is one of the reasons why ceremony and/or sacred drama are so powerful. When the ceremonialist invokes/evokes using their voice, when they imagine the beings evoked coming towards them and sense and weave the energy

2 Naydler, Jeremy, Shamanic Wisdom in the Pyramid Texts: The Mystical Tradition of Ancient Egypt, Inner Traditions, 2004.

with thought, sound, breath and intention, the basic ingredients for creation, magick and transformation are present. Many spiritual/magickal practitioners state that ceremony is everything. (Mind you, we say that about intention and sound too.) Sound and intention are usually present in ceremony. Some ceremony of course is silent, but silence has no meaning, no definition, save the absence of sound.

Chapter Seven is initiatory and ecstatic; collectively we build an astral temple with invocation, sound, visualisation in a ritual setting. Everyone is masked and robed and invites beings to be present in the temple. The temple is placed on the astral and guarded by four elemental dragons of fire, water, air and earth. Each student is taught how to access and work within the temple for their own private development, away from the classes. The experience is both devotional and magical and appears to me to deeply transform the student's experience of spirit and their own personal growth.

Invocation using sound has a further purpose; the vibratory nature of sound alters matter at many levels. If a violin is played next to a silent grand piano, piano strings will sound. The vibrations are matched by the same vibratory potential in other matter. Sound made by a healer with gongs, crystal bowl, the human voice and other tools can and does create healing in the body. As a healer, I invoke divinity and Spirit into the body of my client. I make a sound similar to that of a chant, which vibrates in my body, and with the sound and my intention, induces healing in my client. Chung Fu taught me a form of healing that seems to me to prove over and over again to be transformative, powerful and effective. I call it Deep Wound Healing or Deep Spiritual Healing and use it throughout the spiritual development courses. As a singer, performer and writer of spiritual songs, I use a combination of my music and deep trance to induce change, growth and spiritual development.

So onward now, onward to Mona in the first century with Danaray.

CHAPTER ONE

MEETING YOUR SPIRIT GUIDES

IMOGEN WALKED into the centre of the circle, naked and proud: naked that is apart from the tiara on her head that encompassed the cow horns and the blue woad that smudged areas of her body. Tonight, with the circle of dreamers and with the help of the elfin druid brothers, she would summon the Lord of the Wildwood, invoke the raw masculine power of the god, he who rips with tooth and horn. Tonight was the Libran full moon. However, with the roaring sacred fire at the centre of the Oak Grove, and the building of the divine energy of magic, she felt little of the cold despite her nakedness. Her eight sisters were dancing and chanting, naked and ecstatic, awaiting the elfin druids who would form the outer circle and with them build and direct the energy to Imogen and her consort, Markseyer, the eye that knows, the inner eye that sees.

In these times, the initiated were still honoured with direct connection with elemental beings. They could see and share the magic of the great mother with other spiritual inhabitants of this sacred land. Markseyer was an elf, a shining one, a being of the land. He was to be present to invoke the warrior goddess, to call her down from the Libran Moon into the body of Danaray the Dreamer, to embody the raw masculine power of the god. For tonight the lord and the lady and the power animals were to walk the land and terrify the armies of Rome. So great was the energy of the wrath from the divine parents, and focused against those who dared to plunder their home and abuse their children, it was also focused on the masculine force that wrought havoc. Who dared to plunder their home and abuse their children? Who was this masculine force that wrought havoc on the divine balance and claimed sole divinity for himself?

As the ecstatic dance reached divine pitch, Danaray/ Imogen could faintly hear the drums of the Earth; the druids were coming and divine union would be known tonight. The drums, rhythmically interweaving with the sound of stamping feet, along with the sexual energy of divine union raised the temperature as the feminine and masculine raw energy danced together in a perfect dissonance of harmony. Feminine and masculine sound filled the sacred circle as Imogen stepped forward audacious, embodying spirit and kundalini, in full trance, eyes ablaze, and with the commanding voice of a magician, called out to the land:

I invoke thee: Oh wild god of tooth and claw,
Unrefined driving force of nature.
Great divine energy of raw masculinity,
Wild and powerful horned one,
Come render, destroyer, ripper and

God of the Sabbat.
Come king of the wild wood,
Come with your sexual energy of Roodmass.
I invoke thee tall, muscular, virile and
Naked lord.

Come with your feral eyes of the wolf
And your power of dissolution, death and decay.
Bring your energy of terror, chaos and madness
To visit on the soldiers of Rome who rape
And pillage your land and people.
Come lord of the mound with your elusiveness,
With your immense terror and panic.
Come great sum and accumulation of the
Knowledge of our ancestors.
Come elfin king of Avalon, great archetypal
Wizard and shaman,
Learned in all things and wise beyond measure.

Come lord of wisdom, knowledge, life and
fecundity,
The great darkness and light.
Come Master of Light, you who enlivens,
Illuminates and gives life to the world.
Come light bearer and teacher of humankind.
I invoke thee, great motivator of the higher faculties
Of the soul, the highest manifestor of divine power.
Be here great god in our time of need.

The land began to rumble and shake and the flames
of the fire hissed and crackled reaching an intensity of
masculinity. Terror was visited on all present, but they
stood their ground, resolute in their purpose, strong
and powerful and sexually aroused.

Markseyer, the Shining One, tilted his head back and

appeared to grow in stature and power due to the power coursing through him His eyes became wild and his voice a growl of articulation and raw unrefined power. In the sacred circle all could see the antlers of the elfin king of Avalon and Mona, Great lord of Darkness and Bringer of Light. All present saw and felt his energy, so utterly did it dominate them, and all present with their magic and intention directed the energy into the body of Marseyer the elf.

With a voice of fire, the Lord of the Wildwood stepped forward. All present, apart from Imogen, moved rhythmically around the edge of the sacred circle, stamping and chanting, bodies ablaze with energy. Imogen stood still, proud, naked completely focused in trance awaiting Briga the Goddess of the Moon into Imogen's yet still fragile human frame. And through the beating drums, the stamping and calls of invocation came the booming voice of the Lord of the Mound:

I invoke thee great Briga, goddess of the Moon.
As your consort I invoke thee in your aspect of
The terrible.
Come bringer of death, regeneration, healing and
rebirth,
You who spells the end of the Age of Taurus.
Come great white sow who devours the souls of the
dead.
Come with your rage, oh great mother, destroyer of
those
Beings who threaten your children and your land.

Great dark Moon, full Moon and pregnant Moon,
Crone, Callieach of winter, goddess of the
underworld.

Be here with your fire, your sickle and your sword, you
Who cuts all life.
Come as Ceridwen and Shelia–na-gig, goddess of the
Open yoni of transformation.
Come as the hawk who hovers still in the eye of the
Storm awaiting her prey.
Come as the raging winds of the storm.
Come as Danu of the earth, the bone woman, the
stone woman.
Come ancient ancestor of these lands, you who rules
When the veils are the thinnest between this world
and the next.
Come great alpha female, great warrior goddess.
Come you who accompanies your dreamers.
I invoke thee, great Beansidhe cry of death,
Great mother of all things who we are emanations of.
Come Briga, great wild one, mother of the tribes,
Sacred goddess of these lands.
Bring your wrath to destroy the armies of the eagle
and followers of the bull.
Be here great Briga in the body of your priestess.

The eyes of Briga were fixed and terrible, showing the goddess scorned, the rage of the protectress. She stood commandingly at the centre of the sacred circle and called to the elementals of the land, sky, fire and rivers. She commanded the spirits of the animals and armies of the ancestors. The chanting, stamping, dancing and energy of the sisters and the druids reached fever pitch and suddenly, with a change of rhythm, all collapsed exhausted to the ground, releasing the magic to accompany the armies of the tribes of Britannia.

Psychic Development Course

Lesson One

1. Journeying to the spirit worlds to meet your spirit guides
2. Working with your spirit guides in this world
3. Working with voice, vision, feeling, sounding and breathing techniques – the art of ritual and ceremony
4. Prayer and the imagination gateway
5. Working with psychometry, grounding and centring

Class activity: Grounding and centring exercise

Standing in a circle hand in hand, left hand facing upwards to receive, right hand downward in a giving mudra:

Closing your eyes, focus your attention on your heart

chakra. Send a beam of light down from your heart, journeying down with it, down through your body and down through the floor. Down through the layers of the building you are in and down, down into the earth. Down through the top layer of the earth, the broken rock and rubble. Down past the tree roots and the bones of our ancestors and down, down at the speed of light through the layers of Mother Earth. Go down, sensing the layers, the colours and the hues of the earth, moving down to the plasma near the core of the earth, down into the molten lava and down into the fire at the very core of Mother Earth.

Reach the fire of life, the fire of all potentiality at the very core of the planet. Allow the fire to burn round and through your body filling your aura, healing and purifying right into the depth of your being.

Now pull the energy of the fire back up the beam of light, up through the molten rock of lava, up through the plasma near the core and up, up through the layers of the earth at the speed of light. Moving back past the bones of the ancestors, the tree roots, the broken rock and rubble and up through the top layer of the earth. Pull the fire up through the layers of this building and feel it spinning through your feet, legs and body and into your heart. Now send a beam of light out of the top of your crown, out through the space between you and the ceiling out through the layers of the building and out into the skies. Pass the clouds and out into the universe, moving at the speed of light through the galaxy and through as many galaxies as you can. See stars, moons, planets and asteroids as you reach for the furthest star that you can possibly imagine.

Feel that star explode and its energy pour down the beam of light, moving through space, moving through the galaxies back, back to your home world, back towards the blue planet, circling the planet, coming over the country that you are in, the city you are in, over the building you are in. Now feel the star energy, the magic of Spirit, descending down through the skies, down through the roof of the building and down into the crown of your head, through your body and into your heart chakra.

Feel the light of Spirit, the star energy mingling with the fire energy from the core of the earth in your heart. Feel your heart chakra opening and see a being of light step forward, one that looks just like you. Send a beam of light from your heart to the heart of this being, take a deep breath and take in your soul.

INVOCATION

I call to my spirit guides. I call to Danaray my twin soul, great magician, great gatekeeper, dearest sister, lady of the cow horns. Bring our sisters: Carona, Tejana, Taniete, Calafae, Taisai and Rhana, Jamena and Lenina. Bring our elfin druid brothers, Marksie, Sephora, Camacea, Concara, Netura, Manasaelia, Nephcurous, Shento and Marsaeo. Come Running Wolf and Arturius, Marianna, Aunt Alice, Seema. Come Chung Fu and the Chinese guides. Come Father Michael my wise one. I call to you my power animals: Miriam, spirit of the white wolf and the spirits of the grey wolf, black panther and grizzly bear. Come condor, buzzard and dark owl. Come my totem animal, the golden eagle, and my beloved personal angel, Mercurial. Be here in this circle with me.

By squeezing the hand of the student on my left I invite each person to invoke their spirit guides and power animals, if they know them, either aloud or silently in their minds, or if not, I invite them to invite the presence of guides and power animals and ask to find a way of consciously remembering who they are. Sound is a primary spiritual tool, a connection to Spirit that with practice you begin to experience tangibly. Sound increases sensitivity to Spirit and reduces boundaries that affect conscious manifestation of choice and increase a sense of well being.

Sound is an integral part of many spiritual traditions: druidic, Wiccan and other pagan practices, Hinduism, Buddhism and Christianity (particularly in relation to mantra), ancient Egyptian magic and devotional have all used sound. Many tribal rituals across the world understood/understand the nature of sound. Islam and Sufism (its mystic wing) have a unique relationship with sound and the ninety-nine names of Allah. Practicing Jews and adherents to the Qabalah chant divine names and, along with Muslims and Christians, regard sound as a fundamental part of the creation story:

"And God said let there be light," – the *Torah* and the *Old Testament*

"In the beginning was the word," – the *New Testament*

Hindus understand that the sound *om* launched the beginning of the universe.

Although at the beginning of the introductory course I allow students to silently invoke or, more usually ask, Spirit to be present, I actively encourage all students to make sound, prose, poetry, song or just noises to invoke. Calling to your guides, angels, power animals, divinity and anything else, sets up another level of connection with Spirit that is often being sought by the student.

Take a deep breath, let it go, breathe in again and as you breathe out send a beam of light from your heart to the hearts of all here in this circle. Breathe in again, and this time as you breathe out send a ray of light from your third eye to the third eye of all in the circle. One more time, breathe in together and as you release your breath send a ray of light to the centre of the circle to a point about a foot above us where we all energetically connect. Make sound, activate your vision, see rays of light, activate your imagination, see, feel, hear Spirit joining our sacred circle. Breath is also a fundamental tool; it is the crossover from the conscious to the unconscious. Breath is Spirit, the breath of life, inspiration, creativity, the place where we know none of us is ever really separate, for as we stand together with Spirit, together in circle, we each breathe in and out millions of anti-bodies, millions of molecules, until it is impossible to tell which of the micro–organisms of breath belongs to me and which belongs to you.

Breath allows access to the subconscious and the supraconscious, the soul and its relationship to the divine, the All. Its use allows us to consciously navigate our attention to other places of our perception. Intention, focus and breath heals, remembers and accesses emotion, the very experience of life. As we breathe, we constantly change our physical composition. We are literally, physically, not the people we were just a few minutes ago. We have evolved; we have called forth a new experience of who we are. Even when the logic of atrophy reaches its climax, we say that we have died. Our breath molecules live on in others, our genes in our offspring and our memories in all whose paths we have touched.

For breath is a microcosm of the All, for the ever changing experience comes from inspiration and its external manifestation-exhalation. As the divine inhaled, the inspiration to experience itself occurred, and as she exhaled, the manifestation of the illusion of separation, being able to experience himself as separate parts at every level happened, micro and macro and the universe expanded. Over billions of years, when every aspect of the divine had been experienced in every possible way within that particular exhalation, she inhaled again seeking further inspiration of the divine possibility of all things expressed in the great supraconsciousness. This supraconsciousness was accessed by the breath, and limited or expanded by the divine imagination itself, spiralling through the nothingness of space with linear intent until all was broken down and returned to the source of nothingness, to become the everything again with each exhalation.

Balance always returns; it is natural law. The yin and yang are not separate, but are equal expressions of all that there is. That which is has no meaning in the absence of that which is not. The darkness is the energy that holds the light. The experience of our soul families is an experience of both 'That which is' and 'That which is not'. Our soul mates (the experience, that which is) and our spirit guides (the knowing, that which is not) demonstrate this concept. Through the breath, the imagination (the gateway to spirit) the intention and the light, we can know that which is not (spirit guides) and hence that which is not becomes that which is. Like our physical experience of separation from the All, in which our uniqueness is expressed, illusion and reality become one and the divine experiences itself in all of its magnificence. Whilst our spirit guides, power animals and angels are not the divine in its ultimate sense, neither are they intermediaries for the divine. They are expressions of the divine experiencing herself at that level of consciousness and hence are the divine expression her/himself.

31

CLASS ACTIVITY: JOURNEY TO MEET YOUR SPIRIT GUIDES

Take a deep breath and allow your eyes to fall closed. Follow your breath around your body with your mind and relax as you breathe out. Again, breathe in following your breath around your body with your mind and, while breathing out, relax. One more time breathe in, follow your breath around your body with your mind and relax as you breathe out. Focus your attention now on the place where the air meets your nose, breathing in, breathing out, relaxing your body, focussing your attention on the point where the air meets your nose, breathing in, breathing out relax. One more time, focus your attention on the point where the air meets your nose, breathing in, breathing out, relax.

As you breathe in, imagine a beam of light coming from the heavens, filling your body through the crown of your head and surrounding the outside of your body like a fluffy cloud as peace, calm and relaxation fill your being. Again, breathe in the beam of light filling and surrounding your body like a fluffy cloud as peace, calm and relaxation fill your being. One more time, breathe in the beam of light, filling and surrounding your body like a fluffy cloud as peace, calm and relaxation fills your being.

On your in breath, keep breathing in the light. On your out breath, exhale a thick mist as worry, fear and restlessness move far away from you to be transformed by Mother Universe. Again, breathe in the light, breathe out the mist as worry, fear and restlessness float far away from you to be transformed by Mother Universe. One more time, breathe in the light and exhale the mist as worry, fear and restlessness move far away from you.

Feel relaxation spread down from the crown of your

head, down through your head and face. Feel your jaw relax, and relax the front of your throat and the back of your neck. Relaxing your shoulders, feel relaxation spread down the front of your body and down your spine, down through your thighs and down your legs and into your feet and toes.

Imagine you have a screen in your mind and on that screen you can see the number thirteen. Imagine the numbers twelve, eleven and ten drifting deeper down. Nine, eight and seven down, down, down. Six, five and four, drifting down deeper now. Three, two and one, deep, deep, deep relaxation.

In front of you is a dark brown oak door with your name on it on a golden plaque. Pass through the doorway, closing the door behind you. On the screen of your mind see a large meadow. At its centre is an ancient rock, and trees extend around the circumference of the meadow. The screen of your mind is merely a veil between this world and the next. Pass through the veil now and find yourself on the outskirts of the meadow between the trees. Place your hands on their bark and feel the textures, sense the breeze rustling in the leaves and smell their aroma in the air.

Walk through the meadow now, feeling the grass under your feet, a slight breeze on your face and the sun on your back on a late pleasant afternoon. As your reach the ancient rock, place your hands on the stone, feel its age, wisdom and knowledge. With your back to the rock, turn and face north (the direction faced first alters with the time of year, I am writing this part at Yule). Silently, in your mind, repeat after me:

I call to the powers of the north, the powers of air, the powers of Spirit. I call to the eagle and the owl, the condor and the buzzard and the wren, the king of the birds.

See these creatures flying towards you from the northern horizon. When they reach about two metres in front of you, see them stop, ask them to stay and build your sacred circle. With your back still to the rock turn and face the east, silently in your mind repeat after me:

I call to the powers of the east the powers of fire, the powers of the mind, I call to the mother bear who gave birth to the human race. The cat, the Moon hare, the green woodpecker and the red hen who lays the eggs of potentiality. See these creatures coming towards you from the eastern horizon, and when they reach about two metres in front of you see them stop, ask them to stay and build your sacred circle.

With your back to the rock turn now and face the south, silently in your mind repeat after me:

I call to the powers of the south, the power of water, the power of emotion. I call to the whale of knowledge, the salmon of wisdom, the playful dolphins. I call to the beaver, otter and the seal."

See these creatures swimming towards you from the southern horizon, and when they reach about two metres in front of you see them stop, ask them to stay and build your sacred circle. With your back still to the rock turn and face the west. Silently in your mind repeat after me:

I call to the powers of the west, the powers of earth, the powers of physicality. I call to the fox, the badger and the wild boar. I call to the mole and the blackbird.'

See these creatures coming towards you from the western horizon and when they reach about two metres in front of you see them stop, ask them to stay and build your sacred circle. Now facing the rock in the centre repeat silently after me:

By the power of three times three,
I call my spirit guides to me.
By the power of three times three,
I call my spirit guides to me.
By the power of three times three,
I call my spirit guides to me.

See beings made of light and taking human form begin to manifest in front of you. Use your mind like a zoom lens on a camera, zooming in and out. Give yourself permission to see them, hear them, feel them and sense them. Whichever way that you sense spirit, allow that to be correct. Amplify the way that you perceive in this situation. Sharpen, brighten, dim, move nearer to or further away. Activate your taste, smell and emotion. Ask your guides to help you by matching your vibration.

Ask your spirit guides questions. What are their names? Which one is your gatekeeper? What roles are they playing in your spiritual development? How can you connect with them when working alone? What past lives did you experience with spirit guides who are present? What can they tell you about your spiritual path in this life?

Listen to anything they have to tell you in any way you experience their communication.

If you are having any difficulties experiencing your spirit guides, see Pegasus the white horse fly down into the centre of the sacred circle. Climb on his back and fly up, up and out to the top of a mountain overlooking the sacred circle. Climb off his back and await the arrival of your guides. Ask the questions written above.

If you have flown to the top of the mountain, thank and release your guides, summon Pegasus, climb on his back and fly back down to the sacred circle. If you stayed in the circle, thank and release your guides.

With your back to the rock facing the north, thank and release the large birds. See them fly away to the north and vanish on the horizon. With your back still to the rock, turn and face the east, thank and release the mother bear, the green woodpecker, the red hen, the Moon hare and the cat. See them leave to the east and vanish on the horizon. With your back still to the rock, turn and face the south, thank and release the large fish and water mammals, see them swim away and vanish on the horizon in the south. With your back to the rock turn and face the west, thank and release the creatures of the earth, see them vanish on the western horizon.

Walk back through the meadow and pass back through the screen of your mind. See the dark brown oak door with the golden plaque with your name on it. Open the door, pass through the doorway closing the door behind you. Coming back up the steps one, two, three, four, five, feel the energy spinning up through your feet and legs. Six, seven, eight, feel the energy in your body. Nine, ten, eleven, twelve, feel the energy in your head and face. In a moment I will say thirteen and you will open your eyes, remember everything and feel completely in your body and grounded. Thirteen – open your eyes, come back, remember!

Some students, when they return from these kinds of spiritual journeys, feel dizzy or light-headed, disorientated or not in their bodies. I show them how to ground themselves by sending a beam of light from their heart chakras to the fire at the core of the earth and bringing the energy of the fire back into the heart chakra. Going from the heart to the fire at the core of Mother Earth is one grounding technique. Sending light from the heart chakra down to the fire at the core, back to the heart chakra and then up to the highest star and back to the heart chakra is known as grounding and centring.

For me, any spiritual work, whether ceremonial/ ritual, shamanic journeying, magick or clairvoyance/ mediumship, is far more focused when the practitioner is grounded and centred first. Chung Fu tells me that everything happens from the centre. Grounding is vitally important when following any spirit or conducting energetic working, which many of us have learned the hard way by either ignoring or misunderstanding the importance of grounding. Connecting with Spirit alters the energetic vibrations in our bodies, disturbing our emotional and cognitive experiences and thus causing us to manifest our realities in disturbed ways unless these energies are appropriately integrated. Grounding into Mother Earth is for me the most powerful way of doing this, for Mother Earth is the provider and the protectress, the manifestor of our dreams and our creations. From her came all life on this planet and her core fire is the great alchemist, the energy with which all vibrations are integrated. Some traditions and/or spiritual teachers use the idea of imagining tree roots coming from the soles of your feet or from your base chakra and going down into the earth. These visualisations work fine; it is just that I prefer the depth, quantity and quality of the energy from the latent kundalini of Gaia.

The key to spirit is imagination itself, because there is no separation. The moment that you imagine your guides one way, that is the way that they appear. Indeed, the concept of something being *just my imagination* assumes that that creative spark cannot have been initiated by Spirit itself. At times students will say to me, *Did I really see that or did I make it up?* My answer to both questions is, "Yes, this is the creative tool that spirit uses to connect with you."

When working with spirit through meditation, path working and ritual, allow yourself to internally perceive in whatever way is natural to you. If you see spirit but don't hear spirit, make that OK and delve deeper into the visual. If you feel Spirit but don't see it, that is OK too. Dig deeper into the feeling. Try not to make your senses wrong by refusing to validate your experience and reaching for another internal perceptual experience before you agree that you have had an experience of Spirit. Trust everything you receive and don't be afraid to be wrong.

Neuro–Linguistic Programming (NLP) relies on the idea of building rapport which identifies how an individual thinks, how their thought processes work. Some people are mainly visual in their thinking processes, others kinaesethic, yet others auditory. A trainer or therapist can identify which the client or patient is by encouraging the individual to verbally express something they are passionate about and listen to the metaphors they use. *I get the picture ... it is crystal clear etc.* begins to suggest that the individual thinks in a primarily visual way. *I hear you, it rings a bell etc.* suggests auditory thinking and *I get a feeling ... the energy is ... or the vibes* suggests a kinaesthetic thought process. I am primarily kinaesthetic and closely secondly visual. Very few of us experience one internal sense alone. Working with Spirit, I have found that this idea also applies to how we experience the spiritual; seeing, feeling or hearing spirit are all equally appropriate.

As an adult, when I started again to consciously work with Spirit my first experiences were visual/feeling. It was a good many months later that I experienced Spirit auditorily. The internal senses are very subtle. Kathy Jones, a teacher of mine, describes her experiences as see/feel. She neither sees Spirit nor feels Spirit, but experiences it somewhere in between. I understand completely what she means.

When my spirit guides speak to me, I know exactly which one is talking (by the tone of their voice, accent etc.) yet the voice speaks silently in my mind. I know exactly what Danaray looks like; I recognise the details of her face when she appears as Imogen or Jessica, yet the experience is a subtle see/feel. See/feel, although subtle, is undeniably powerful for me although its subtlety in no way suggests an absence of the experience of Spirit; it is just the nature of Spirit. *That which is, that which is not.* As Kathy has often said, *Trust everything you get and don't be afraid to be wrong.*

Working with Spirit will lead the individual into crisis; that is the one thing I feel confident promising my students. Most students don't take me that seriously, or they think I am in some way speaking figuratively, but into crisis eventually they go. For us to become a clear channel for Spirit, it is necessary for Spirit to work through our emotional bodies, releasing repressed emotion which then we often re-experience as it moves through our external realities. I asked my spirit guides why it is that transformation comes only through crisis. They laughed and replied, It *doesn't, beloved. Transformation can come from joy, but let's face it, you are hardly ready for joy.*

CLASS ACTIVITY: PSYCHOMETRY

I invite students to work in pairs to practice psychometry. I enjoy teaching psychometry at the beginning of the introductory level of my courses, because most of my students experience connection and/or information from Spirit almost immediately and hence are much encouraged. Psychometry involves holding an item belonging to their working partner, I usually suggest in the palm of their left hand as we receive with our left hands. Often images, feelings or sounds/words occur in the mind of the reader very quickly. I encourage the reader to speak immediately about whatever they experience, as the act of speaking brings further information.

The idea of psychometry is that objects hold energetic imprints of the person who owns the object. By holding that item, your focus collapses any separation between you and their energetic imprint wave patterns and you have access to its knowledge. As with meditation and shamanic journeying work, the information you see, hear and/or feel may be subtle, again allow that to be OK. As soon as you receive any information, even if it is a feeling or a colour, speak it. The act of verbal communication opens up the channels for Spirit to flow. Other clarity techniques in relation to psychometry include imagining that with a sharp deep inhalation of breath, you breathe in information from the item up your arm and into your third eye chakra.

Feedback and clarification of the experiences of Spirit are included throughout the class. We close the session with a grounding session and a prayer of thanks, releasing Spirit and sometimes using sacred sound, depending on the energy present.

CHAPTER TWO

THE POWER ANIMALS AND THE SHAMANIC LOWER WORLDS

THE RELEASE OF magical energy was exhausting for Imogen. At times, the priestesshood was so demanding. She longed for peace in these troubled times, for the connection of love, the All, the love of the great divine. She was aware that she had chosen her role and the responsibilities of the dreamer priestess of these lands, and she knew deep within her being that this age was coming to an end.

Her dreams of late had had a sense of foreboding. She knew, but did not choose to share with others, that victory over the Romans was but a temporary aberration and that the rage of the bull would prevail. She was aware of deeper messages, happening in lands afar that would end the Age of Taurus the bull, but not the Age of the Romans. The Roman emperors were the instrument that would eventually slaughter the bull of Taurus and herald the coming of the Age of Pisces Imogen had seen this truth in the stars and in her scrying in the rivers of this land.

The druids had seen the coming of the godman for hundreds of years. This godman was different from any other divinity that she knew however, for his coming and his passing repressed and denied all other understandings and experiences of the divine. This confused Imogen, for deep within her meditations she knew that it was not the godman himself, but the power built upon his execution that so distorted the nature of the divine mother and father.

Three weeks had passed since the Aries full moon and already the movement of the clouds, the flight of the birds and the rumblings of the land told her that the great armies of Rome were gathering again. She wondered how long Mona would survive. Imogen had almost completely isolated herself since that night of magic. Well, at least she had isolated herself from human company. Markseyer had spoken to her a number of times in the forest and she had meditated and talked extensively to Spirit.

Her mother, also named Imogen, had been at the head of the dreamers and very influential in the tribes. Her ritual magic was renowned for its creativity, focus, originality and power, and her wisdom sought in many situations. Imogen had been trained by her mother and, where appropriate, worked with the circle of dreamers in her childhood, each member of the nine contributing to her education. For it had always been known from the days of Imogen's grandmother and great grandmother that Julius Caesar would not be the last Roman emperor to invade the Isles of Brigit and those with sight had foretold the stories of Imogen, archdruidess of the dreamers for many years before her birth.

Imogen had yearned to be close to her mother. It was a yearning that she had always known, yet her mother had always been so unreachable, so aloof; an archdruidess but never her mother. For Imogen, both as a child and a woman, the empty hole deep in her being had always been filled by her personal experience of dreaming, of magic. Imogen would chastise herself, tell herself that that was simply the nature of her reality, but in her times of reflection her experience of the lady of the forest, the divine spirit of the land, was also filled with feelings of both longing and rejection. Imogen had given her whole life to the goddess, but the wound felt as if it had festered, so deeply had it embedded itself.

Silently in her mind she could hear Markseyer calling to her, calling to her from the lands of the fey. She had resisted journeying, she had given so much energy, so much rage in magical warfare against the hated armies of Rome, but still they came, still they destroyed all in their path! Why, why did the goddess allow this? Would Bridie be the enigma that her own earthly mother had always been? Again she heard Markseyer calling.

Imogen knew that she must journey to the land of the fairie. Her energy and emotion was still low, but she had responsibility for the welfare of the tribes, she could not afford to lack the full strength of her magic. Resigned, Imogen found the largest oak tree in that part of the forest, the tree that she knew so well. With her mind she sought the chief dyad of that place: "Great dyad spirit of this forest, old friend be here," she cried out. "I am Danaray; I am your kith and kin. Grant me access through your being to the place of the shining ones, for my brother Markseyer calls to me."

An ancient male face of root and twig, branch and green foliage appeared in her mind's eye. Imogen sensed the concern of her old friend; he reported destruction and burnings of parts of the forest sixty leagues further south. The sons of men from another land who showed no regard for the trees, plants and animal folk of these sacred hills and fern and wrought sacrilege and violence on this sacred land. Of course, access was granted immediately.

Imogen stood legs apart and arms raised in the shape of a V; her limbs the four elements: fire (sey), air (bre), water (gan), earth (canara) and the place of her heart, ether, the great spirit. She sent her inner sight to the fire at the core of the land, gathering its energy and drawing the flame back to her heart. She sent her consciousness through her crown out to the furthest star of her imagination and drew its massive power back through the cosmos back to her heart. Mingling the energies of the land and the heavens in her heart, she used her breath to expand her auric bodies until she was the size of the universe.

From this place of the infinite universe, she saw a blinding light gathering above her head. A beam of that light descended down through her body, down deep into Mother Earth, as she vibrated the name of the sacred goddess Eostra, she whose mantle is the stars, through her being.

Drawing the light from the land again up the centre of her body, she vibrated the name Ceridwen, the crone of the underworld. Divine light poured up her left leg, diagonally across her body and out through her extended right arm, out to infinity, as she vibrated the name Bridie, the ancestral maiden goddess of these isles.

Pulling the divine light with her mind through her right leg, she vibrated the sacred goddess Bloudewedd the owl and as the light diagonally crossed her body and passed out through her extended left, out to infinity, she vibrated the sacred name of the great mother Madron. Imogen saw and felt herself as the five pointed star, the sacred pentacle shining in the heavens, filled with divine power.

Sitting with her back resting against the oak tree, the back of her head resting against the trunk, Imogen closed her eyes and transferred her spirit into the tree. She saw herself swimming rapidly in a fast downhill flowing river which plunged into a great lake below. At the bottom of the lake she immediately recognised the underwater cave that she regularly used to access the lower world. Eventually, as she swam through the cave, she became more and more aware of how shallow the water was becoming. Soon Imogen was swimming again on the surface of the water, swimming in a river that opened out from the back of the cave into the worlds and forests of the fairie.

Imogen swan to the left bank of the river and pulled herself out of the water into the fairie forest. In a familiar clearing ahead, she saw a white wolf waiting for her. In joy she called to her friend Miriam, who responded by nestling her head into Imogen's hand. Other power animals began to join Imogen, the eagle of the mountains, the dark owl and the grizzly bear. Imogen called to her gatekeeper, a dear old friend of the world of spirit, the priest from Avalon, the man who spoke to the bears, Arturius magician of alchemy and magic. A hooded cloaked figure stood in front of her radiating magic from every pore of his body of light.

"Come Danaray," he said telepathically and he led the way briskly down one of the paths deep into the forest, deep into the darkness. It felt as if they had walked for hours and the forest seemed to become denser. Imogen was still unsure when Markseyer would appear; indeed if he would appear at all. She found herself deep in thought remembering the last ritual, the magic that they had done together in the oak grove, the energy she had raised, her nakedness, the rage ...

Imogen brought her consciousness back to the fairie forest and realised that she was alone – Arturius and her power animals were not in reach of her mind. She experienced slight irritation with herself; she had allowed her focus to drift and now she was walking alone. Suddenly, in the distance to her left, she caught a glimpse of Markseyer. She rushed through the trees towards where she thought she had seen him, but no, the clearing was empty.

Imogen knelt on the ground in the clearing, closed her eyes and waited. Deeper and deeper in trance she drifted, waiting, waiting for Markseyer.

"Danaray," she heard Markseyer's voice whisper. "Open your eyes Danaray."

In front of her Imogen saw Markseyer. Light enveloped him, held him in a state of blissful focus. His image faded, or rather was consumed by an aura of multi coloured brilliance. She took a few moments to focus; she felt her heart beating wildly in sublime excitement.

"Danaray my child, my darling priestess," the queen of the fairie said. "So hard and painful you make your path, so deep you have chosen for your soul to grow in this life. Yet so deep your maternal wounds, so much anger buried in your fragile body. Chose now beloved for your heart to be open, know my love is always with you."

Imogen's eyes were full of tears as she surveyed the divine being before her. For here was the divine feminine of these lands. Great lady whose antlers held the life giving sun, the goddess whose skin radiated a violet hue and whose aura was of rainbow light.

"Who are you, great mother?" Imogen whispered.

"I am the beginning and the end," said the divine voice that sounded silently of the hills and the forests, of the lakes and the rivers. "I am the lady of the isle of the dead, of paradise and of the sacred lands. I weave the web of

46

time and the universe and I am all of the mysteries. I am the lady of the lake, goddess of the isle of apples. I am the magic that you call forth. I am the whisper of the winds, the roar of the fires. I am the swelling currents of the deep and my fertile body is the sacred land. I am the cycle of life, birth, youthfulness, sexuality and parenthood. It is me who summons death with my beansidhe cry and it is me you will find in the stillness where you wait for rebirth. Close your eyes now Danaray, and receive my blessings and with your dreams and your deep longing. Send my healing to all parts of this fractured land, to the Romans and the tribes."

Sound and light filled Imogen's body and rainbow colours dominated her aura, and, as she filled and expanded, love poured out of her being. She saw the love flow to all the tribes of her lands and beyond, she saw the land come to life and harvests flourish, she saw the rivers flow and heard the hills, valleys and forests sing. She even saw the soldiers of Rome healed and blessed. As Imogen she wanted to resist the blessing of the Romans, as Danaray she knew that all was perfect.

Imogen heard the voice of her deceased earthly mother. As she opened her eyes she saw her mother standing before her. For the first time in her life she experienced her mother as kind, for the first time her longing was silenced.

"Hurry back to your body my child," her mother said. "Hurry back to the land of the living for you are in great danger."

Imogen snapped awake as she heard an arrow whistle past her head and bury itself in the trunk of the tree. As she jumped to her feet and started to run, Imogen felt an arrow pass through and become lodged in her right shoulder. She screamed and called for power, firing a bolt of lightning back with her magic.

PSYCHIC DEVELOPMENT COURSE

LESSON TWO

1. Shamanic journeying to the lower world
2. Working with your power animals
3. Journeying to the lower world of another for healing and information
4. Chakras and breathing; forms of clairvoyant readings
5. Grounding and centring

Grounding and centring he circle begins with participant feedback from the last session. Students who are experiencing each session on a weekly basis often report dreams or clairvoyant/psychic experiences. One of my students told me that I had continued to teach her in her dreams; she also talked of her spirit guides visiting her in her sleep. Some students appear to go into crisis in one way or another within the first week. It is as if Spirit has been waiting to move them on to the next stage of growth and the course is an immediate catalyst. Direct contact with Spirit often brings immediate and lasting healing.

CLASS ACTIVITY

Standing in a circle, each participant holding a hand of each of her neighbours, I invoke my spirit guides and power animals and invite each student in turn to call to spirit either aloud or silently with intention. We activate imagination and use sound and create weaving energy the sewing of the web of light between us all. I lead the meditation/visualisation of sending light and journeying to the fire at the core of the earth.

Standing in the fire at the core of the earth, allow the flames to envelope you, purifying you inside and out. Feel the healing energy of the dark mother coming towards you as the parts of you that no longer serve you die and the spiritual alchemy is born; I invoke her with a song:

Crone, Lady Ceridwen,
Dark goddess of the other world,
Stirrer of the cauldron,
Of the perfect being.
In the darkness of unity,
In the stillness of unity,
Be here, dark lady of death.

Crone Lady Ceridwen,
Mother of crow, sow and toad,
Reaper of death and regeneration,
Give me healing in your darkness
In the underworld.

Steve Wilkes

Be here dark lady of death.
Mother hag cut me down,
With your scissors and sickle,
In the dark days of this old land
When the air is cold
And winter is upon us.
Heal me so I may be reborn.
Crone, Lady Ceridwen,
Dark goddess of the other world.
Take me through the veil
To the beloved souls of our dead.
In the darkness of unity,
In the stillness of unity,
Be here, dark lady of death.

Crone, Lady Ceridwen,
Beloved of our ancestors,
Reaper of the old year,
In the stillness of Samhain.
Give me healing in your darkness
In the underworld.
Be here, dark lady of death.

Mother hag cut me down,
With your scissors and sickle.
In the dark days of this old land,
When the air is cold,
And Stillness is upon us.
Heal me so I may be reborn.

Come, Lady Ceridwen,
Dark goddess of the other world.

Draw the fire energy from the core of Mother Earth back up to your heart and reach for the highest star as per the grounding and centring exercises in Chapter One. Allow the fires of the earth and the heavenly light of spirit to mingle in your heart. Feel your heart chakra opening. See a being of light that looks identical to you take a step forward. Send a beam of light from your heart to the heart of that being. Take a deep breath and breathe in your soul.

Take a deep breath, and, as you exhale, send a beam of light with your breath from your heart to the heart of everyone else in the room. With your next exhaled breath, send a beam of light from your third eye to the third eye of everyone in the room. From your crown chakra, send out light with your breath to the centre of the circle to a point a metre above us where all energetically connect. Make sound, chant, feeling the vibrations of sound in your body. Activate your inner vision, see rays of light as you activate your imagination, see, feel, hear Spirit joining our sacred circle.

A word about shamanic lower worlds: so often students identify them with the Judeo–Christian concepts of the underworlds of hell, and hence fear journeying there. Across history and cultures, the shamanic lower worlds have been demonstrated to be friendly and nothing to do with purgatory or punishment set by a vengeful god. The lower worlds, like many of their inhabitants, are ancient and primal. They are the home of the power animals, many elementals and other ancient supportive spirits. There is nothing to fear from the lower worlds.

Power animals are typically shamanic, ancient primal spirit forms that work with those of us who are visiting and working in the spirit worlds. My power animals accompany me whenever I journey. They keep me safe and advise me as would old friends. In relation to my healing work, I have been assisted by them in reaching very deep, old, repressed emotional wounds in others and in myself. I remember one instance a number of years ago when I found myself walking late at night in south-east London. A number of young men were approaching me in a way that seemed threatening. As they came near, I mentally asked my power animals to surround me as if I were shamanically journeying. All of a sudden the young men took a wide berth, seemingly avoiding contact with me. I am convinced that they were not consciously aware of my power animals, but I am sure they sensed something that left them feeling less than confident.

Every so often I am asked to perform exorcism or building/house clearances. My power animals play a major role in this work, protecting me in situations that can be challenging. I remember once I was asked to a flat belonging to a couple who were disturbed by things being moved and broken, noises (particularly at night), dreams etc. The strangest occurrence related to a spare room they had at the other end of a long corridor. On occasions where there were particularly difficult spirit disturbances, the bedroom door would bang open and closed, but if someone attempted to open the door it would be stuck closed. I experienced this situation during the work, so I sent my power animals into the room first and then I was able to open the door.

I would like to acknowledge the work of other shamanic teachers whose ideas have reinforced or confirmed my own experiences when journeying. Often when journeying to the lower worlds, I have found myself blocked somehow by a physical barrier en route. Leslie Kenton in her book *Journey to Freedom* describes a mud wall blocking her way, calling for help and experiencing a beaver appearing with a sledge hammer to help her. I too have called for help in similar situations, which has always come without fail. However, I have always liked her idea and I felt it was important to mention in case you as a student or reader experience such phenomena.

CLASS ACTIVITY — INTRODUCTORY JOURNEY TO THE LOWER WORLD

As you breathe, let your eyes fall closed. Mentally scan your body, searching for places that may be tense or require further relaxation. Focus on these places and send your breath there to release any tension. Relax your body down and find yourself standing at the top of a flight of stairs.

At the bottom of the flight of stairs is a giant cinema screen. As you take the first step down, the number thirteen flashes across the screen. As you take the next step, the number twelve flashes across the screen. Eleven, ten, nine, drifting down deeper. Eight, seven, six, down, down, down. Five, four, three, drifting down now. Two and one, deep, deep, deep relaxation.

See a dark brown oak door with a golden plaque on it with your name on it. Open the door and pass through the doorway closing the door behind you. On the screen of your mind, see a wooded path leading to a mountain forested from base to peak. The screen of your mind is merely a veil between this world and the next. Pass through the veil and walk the path to the mountain.

Start climbing the mountain path as it weaves up and round the mountain. Become aware of nature around you – long grass, the clicking of crickets, birdsong. Climb up and round, up and round, up, up the mountain. Follow the path up and round until you come across a small clearing with a large boulder on the side of the mountain. Climb up onto the boulder and look out over the panorama, at the other mountains and plains, look out over a sea of tree tops.

Continue climbing up the mountain, up and round, up and round, still noticing plants, insects and birds around you and the crunch of twigs underfoot. Eventually, you find yourself nearing the top of the mountain as you become aware of the sound of rushing water. As you round the path and stand on the peak of the mountain, you see a huge waterfall crashing from the peak down hundreds of metres below, down into a large lake. Swan dive now, throwing yourself into the waterfall, plunging deep down into the lake.

Swim down now, down until you come across a large underwater cave. Swim into the cave and continue to swim down deep into the water along the bottom of the lake. Eventually the water becomes shallower and shallower until you are swimming with your head above water. You find yourself swimming in a large river at the centre of an ancient forest. Swim towards the bank on your left and climb out of the river onto the land. Welcome to the lower world!

One hundred or so metres ahead of you, notice a large rock, on top of which is a creature, an animal or a bird. Approach the creature and silently in your mind and silently in your mind ask it whether it is one of your power animals. If the creature answers yes, ask it to introduce you to other power animals. If the creature says no, ask it to lead you to your power animals. Meet and get to know your power animals. I will come and get you soon.

Your power animals lead you deep into the forest and out towards the other side. You find yourself facing the side of a cliff with steps made of rock carved in its side. Climb up the side of the cliff and walk out over its top looking out over a huge expanse of ocean. High above you see a golden eagle circling. This huge bird circles down and grips you tightly on each shoulder, flying up and out, up and out over the ocean. All of a sudden the eagle lets you go and you fall hundreds of metres down towards the ocean. The eagle swoops down at great speed and catches you, your legs astride its powerful back. Exhilarated, you fly on the back of this giant golden eagle to the heights of the skies. At lightning speed, the eagle tips you off its back and you fall, fall hundreds of metres until the eagle sweeps down and catches you on its back again.

Flying higher and higher to new heights, the eagle carries you, again in a semi-second tipping you from its back, letting you fall hundreds of metres. This time however you feel your neck tip back and your spine arch and you feel yourself fly upwards unaided, you feel the complete freedom of being able to fly. In the spirit worlds all creatures can fly. See your power animals fly out to join you. Fly out across the ocean and explore, map the contours of your lower world. I will come and get you soon.

Fly back now to the place in the forest of your lower world where you entered. Thank and release your power animals and tell them a friend of yours will be visiting them very soon and give your permission for your friend to receive information for you. Dive back into the river and swim back to the cave where you entered the lower world. Swim down into the deep and back through the cave back into the lake. Swim up, up, up to the surface of the lake. Summon your energy and fly to the top of the waterfall at the peak of the mountain.

Wander down the spiral mountain path now, passing the large boulder where you viewed the panorama of trees earlier and continue down the path to the foot of the mountain. Follow the path at the foot of the mountain back through the screen of your mind and open the door with the golden plaque bearing your name. Coming back up the stairs: one, two, three, four, five, six, seven, feel the energy coming up through your feet and legs. Eight, nine, ten, feel the energy in the trunk of your body. Eleven, twelve, feel the energy in your head and face. In a moment I will say thirteen and you will feel yourself completely in your body, grounded, alert and remembering everything. Thirteen, open your eyes, come back, remember!

Often when students return from journeying they feel dizzy or light headed, slightly disorientated or out of their bodies. As a teacher, I check these things and instruct them to ground themselves in the fire at the core of the earth described in chapter one. Alternatively, I imagine figures of eight connecting my crown, heart and root chakras to theirs; these figures of eight are made of light. I imagine that I carry the student to the fire at the core of Mother Earth and back to the heart chakra, completely grounding them.

At this stage we discuss in circle the different experiences each person has had. I have developed the ability to enter into the meditations/journeys of others and observe what is happening. I find that this sometimes helps to clarify how the student interprets their connection with Spirit.

Students often refer to further experiences with their power animals over the next few weeks. These experiences might include suddenly seeing them in nature, in books, paintings or on the television/or at the cinema. It is as if the creatures begin to appear and integrate in ordinary waking reality as well as the shamanic non-ordinary realities. Steven Farmer and other New Age writers have developed websites which give archetypal meanings for power animals. Although these have some usefulness, and hence I would encourage students or readers to look at the archetypes, I would also strongly suggest that the student or reader trusts their own personal connection with their power animals.

FURTHER CLASS ACTIVITY: JOURNEYING FOR OTHERS

I ask students to split into pairs (or threes if there is an odd number in the group) and to take turns journeying to each other's lower worlds for messages and healings from the power animals and even the elementals. The way we organise this is by instructing the student to pass through the oak door with their partner's name on it. Apart from that difference, I encourage the route of the journey to remain the same. Students are very often amazed by the information and knowledge that they receive from their partner's power animals and also how different the lower world of their partner is to that of their own.

I encourage the use of the same route to imprint new neural pathways and build confidence in the student. Of course, there are numerous ways to journey to the lower worlds. Loosely, you journey downwards to the lower worlds and upwards for the higher worlds. Often students say they don't need to go on the journey to reach destinations when they become more experienced with navigating the spirit worlds. However, as the Buddhists say, *The journey is the destination*. And hence so much growth and spiritual confidence is gained by the journey itself.

There was one student I worked extensively with who was very unusual in regards to her relationship with this work. In the guided journeying/meditation she would almost always report not experiencing anything. However, when she journeyed for a partner she was by far my most prolific and able student in terms of the quality of the information she was able to relate. Her clairvoyant and mediumship abilities were also very naturally developed. Information that others received for her almost always reflected that it was important that she learned to receive for herself, that she let go of the need to control everything in her life and that she practiced healing and relaxation. All this information that she received through observation and connection to Spirit I completely agreed with.

CHAKRAS AND BREATHING: FORMS OF CLAIRVOYANT READINGS

I invite students to work in pairs to experience *a chakra and breathing form of clairvoyance* that I learned as a student of Chung Fu's. Due to time restraints, in these particular circles the student gets only a taste of this technique and therefore does not experience the depth of trance and clairvoyant experience that is possible. This particular technique is employed in many occult traditions as well as in meditation and clairvoyance, I return to this technique more intensely in the *Psychic Practitioner Course*.

The student doing the reading inhales slowly for the count of six, holds their breath for the slow count of four and exhales slowly for six. When the student holds their breath for four, they focus attention on the solar plexus chakra of the recipient of the reading. On the in–breath, information is pulled from the solar plexus of the recipient and received in the third eye chakra of the reader, who then holds their breath for four again and focuses their attention on the solar plexus chakra of their partner and the cycle continues.

The circle is closed with prayer, focus and sound, releasing Spirit.

CHAPTER THREE

THE WISE ONE AND THE SHAMANIC HIGHER WORLDS

JANE HAD NOT slept well that night; her dreams had been very disturbed and her magical experience had taught her to be aware of the meaning of her dreams. No-one had seen Imogen for days and overnight Jane had realised that she was unable to sense Imogen – something was very wrong.

It was early morning and the light still had not arrived. Jane slipped into her tunic and cloak and crept out of the hut that she shared with Rebecca and Morgaine and went to the village well. After drawing water and pouring a little into her wooden ceremonial bowl, she returned to the hut and stoked the fire for warmth and light. Jane grounded herself and called to Briga for help. She focussed her mind and stared through the surface of the water, her vision slightly out of focus. Gradually her projected sight in the water took form and she gasped in fear. She could see Imogen lying on a forest floor with an arrow through her shoulder. Imogen appeared very still, however Jane was convinced that she was still alive.

Gathering her emotions and fears, she steeled her determination to help Imogen. Calmly she woke Rebecca and Morgaine, explained what she had experienced and how she planned to respond. The three priestesses summoned their power animals and spirit guides and, after asking for help, left the village and went out in the forest in search of Imogen, not consciously sure which direction to take.

Dawn had broken and the three priestesses ran along the forest path, entirely trusting Spirit to guide them. A fox ran across their path from right to left, slightly diagonally, stopping for a second to look at them before running away. Morgaine recognised her totem animal immediately and led the chase down the new path into denser and denser forest. It wasn't long before they had completely lost sight of the fox. Nonetheless they were experienced enough at connecting with nature to trust their journey. They ran for a good forty minutes until they came across a meeting of paths. Jane reached into a pocket in her tunic and pulled out a handful of dried herbs. With a quick prayer to Ceridwen, she sprinkled the herbs at the crossroads. To the right she briefly thought she saw Arturius, the guide she shared with Imogen, and the three priestesses ran down the right hand path not daring to look back.

They ran for another good half hour and each time they stopped to look, the winds of Moronoe rose and blew leaves and twigs indicating the direction they should go in, pushing them forward. At the edge of the clearing just up ahead Jane saw a white wolf guarding the area. Full of joy she thanked the Green Man, for there was Miriam, her power animal. As they ran towards Miriam the wolf vanished and there, lying almost motionless, was Imogen. All around Imogen was a powerful white light and about ten yards away from her were the burnt remains of three Roman soldiers.

The relieved priestesses gathered around a very weak, barely conscious Imogen. Jane placed her left hand on Imogen's chest feeling her weak heartbeat. She examined Imogen's wound – she had lost a great deal of blood. There were two Roman chargers standing seemingly lost in the clearing. Quickly Jane summoned Markseyer and very soon saw him coming through the trees from behind. Jane sent Rebecca and Morgaine back to the village with instructions to prepare for magic and healing.

Rebecca and Morgaine mounted one of the Roman chargers with ease, after whispering an incantation, and left the other for Jane and Imogen. Markseyer placed herbs and stones on Imogen's body and summoned the healing energy of Mother Earth to channel through his body into Imogen's wounded shoulder. Jane gathered the remains of warm clothing from the Roman soldiers and wrapped them around Imogen, knowing that she would have lost a great deal of body temperature. Rebecca and Morgaine reached the village a good two hours before Jane, Imogen and Markseyer. The journey of the latter had been perilous, as Imogen had kept drifting in and out of consciousness and it was obvious that she was in a great deal of pain, although she never once cried out or spoke of it.

For three days and nights Imogen drifted in and out of consciousness and the priestesses kept a permanent vigil beside her bed. Ceremony and prayer, hot water, rosemary and Bridie's healing energy were a constant part of the healing. Jane journeyed into Imogen's heart chakra and summoned the magic of her ancient soul, the wise one of the higher worlds.

"Great Seybregancanara come, come now and fill my body," she cried out.

She felt her body expand powerfully and angel wings protrude from her back. Experiencing herself as seventy metres tall, full of power she summoned Danaray, her twin soul. Danaray and Seybregancanara journeyed up and out of Imogen's crown chakra. Imogen and Jane, Danaray and Seybregancanara, one being, part of the same soul, passed through one, two, three, four, five, six, seven, eight and nine parallel worlds.

In their parallel hut nine worlds away, Jane saw Imogen standing strong, proud and in full health. From her heart chakra, Jane sent a beam of light to Imogen's heart chakra. From her right palm she sent a beam of light to the world they usually inhabit in ordinary reality, grounding them in materiality. With joy she felt Seybregancanara channel Bridie, the great goddess of healing, and she chanted, "Bridie, Bridie, Bridie," as they journeyed back to Jane's world. On the fourth day Imogen regained full consciousness, her wound totally healed with no indication of the poison of the Roman arrow. Only the emotional scar remained.

Psychic Development Course

Lesson Three

1. Shamanic journeying to the higher world
2. Working with your wise one, your higher self
3. Walking in paradise and connecting with divinity
4. Reading the aura by spinning the chakras
5. Grounding and centring

The shamanic higher worlds, the worlds at the top of the tree and the Axis Mundi are part of the shamanic version of heaven or the heavens. Many commentators experience the higher worlds as different layers of reality and passing through these layers requires one to pass through energy veils, invisible curtains separating different aspects of non–ordinary reality. I certainly experience the higher worlds as layered, and pass through one layer of reality to reach the next.

The higher worlds are ethereal; their beings often appear more detached and less symbolic than those experienced in other worlds when it comes to the content of their messages. Sometimes the beings of the higher world appear as pure light with no other defining features. At other times they come as angels, the wise one, aspects of divinity and/or archetypal figures. Here is the Christian/Islamic/Judaic heaven or paradise. Here is the Buddhist nirvana, the angelic realms, the universe of the spirit guides, the starry worlds, the lands of clouds and dreams, the land of milk and honey. Here are the layers and layers of spirit, the worlds we walk after death. Here are the astral planes where all magic is made before it materialises and manifests in the world of physicality. And here, my friend, is paradise where all is possible, the place of growth, the higher self, initiation and the unity of all things.

As in all classes the circle opens with feedback from participants about their own experiences both in circle and during the time between classes. Often, when I have had access to the teaching room with significant amounts of time before the circle, I have smudged the room with white sage or etheric cleaning agents and very often used sound. Sometimes, ceremonially I have invoked my spirit guides, angels, power animals and the Wheel of Brigitana into the space. At other times I have chanted a Vedic or Buddhist mantra, a favourite being:

Om Tara Tuttare,
Turrae Sohan –
Great mother of the universe,
Provide for all of our needs.

This serves to clear negativity and latent energy from the space and create an environment conducive for love, growth and sublime spiritual experience. The circle again starts with evocation/invocation of the spirit beings that are working with us. I can't emphasise enough how important this process is. It is the glue that connects our spirit guides and other beings to us. We use sound, visualisation, breath and intention to build the energy. We ground and centre by journeying to the fire at the core of Mother Earth and to the furthest star we can possibly imagine, centring the energy in the chakras of our hearts as they open and our souls emerge.

THE HIGHER SELF, GUARDIAN ANGEL, SHAMANIC WISE ONE AND PERCEPTION

The higher self, or the holy guardian angel, experienced by ceremonial magicians is often related to the higher worlds. There is a number of traditions that regards spirit guides and other beings that work with the individual as part of the higher self. Whilst I accept that my guides and my angel Mercurial are at one level part of my higher self, I also experience them as distinct beings in their own right. Chung Fu once described to me the experience in spirit as both one of the collective and one of the unique. Spirit guides take individual personalities relating to particular human lives they have lived in order to communicate effectively with us and also to work out their own karmic obligations.

I experience my higher self as an aspect of divinity who works with my spirit beings in relation to my evolution. Doreen Virtue in her book *Divine Magic* talks about how we are not divinity but there is no part of us that is not divinity. To paraphrase her example (and perhaps simplify it), the big toe on your right foot is not you, however there is no part of the big toe on your right foot that is not you. As I said in the introduction, the divine, the Lady of Avalon, Apollo, the universe, the being of ten thousand names is everything. This is the meaning of omnipresence; in all places in all times, there is not a place that it is not. As Neal Donald Walsh describes in his *Conversations with God,* the divine is always in all ways.

My higher self (or your higher self) is the divine that experiences being everything through the software that I call Steve (or you call whatever name you use). Although through convention that we call shared experience, we may agree to label an experience with the same name, there is no way that we can know that we have actually had the same experience. For example, if we can agree that at present I am wearing an orange pullover (and let us be honest here often we don't agree colour), the experience that I may call my orange pullover and you may call my orange sweater is probably not the same.

Flies, it appears, have a wide visual range, bats experience reality through sound and echo and canines primarily through smell. Reality is merely an experience of perception. Furthermore, perception itself appears to be psychological and much of the perceptive data we do not register consciously. There is a story (which I am told is actually an urban myth) that demonstrates this truth. When Christopher Columbus came across the Americas, as his ship was approaching land the native tribes people were unable to see the ship as they had no experiential reference to know what a ship was.

Through my perspective software, my psychology, my belief systems, past experience, my genetics, my past lives, my culture, my memory, my spiritual awareness and my physical health – how I experience my reality is entirely unique to me. I experience my higher self as the expression of my divinity. In order for my higher self to experience itself in all of its glory, it created my soul which in turn created the bodies and the minds that I have inhabited through time. My higher self is the director of the spiritual evolutionary experience, the journey that I am on. My lower self is the vehicle through which I am realising the All, living consciously and ultimately the journey of my higher self.

Because my higher self, my wise one, my shamanic spirit, my guardian angel, is divinity, by its nature it is the creator, the creator of reality. An exercise of manifestation that I work with was taught to me by Chung Fu.

HIGHER SELF MANIFESTATION EXERCISE

Imagine a massive being of light coming through space and time, coming through the universe. This being is a giant version of you, made of you, made purely of divine light.

See this being hovering over and circling Mother Earth. See it come over the country that you are in, the place that you are in. See your higher self come down through the ether, down through your crown chakra, down through your ajan chakra, your throat chakra and down into your heart chakra.

Send your higher self out through your heart chakra out through time, through the day in front of you, the week in ahead. If there is anything that you are choosing to manifest, see your higher self, as you, receiving it.

As your higher self is divinity, it is absolute. By its nature it is unable to co–exist within your lower self limitations. Many of our difficulties, our wounds, are repressed in the lower three chakras. If we take our higher self down into our lower chakras, it is likely to expel our limitations and we may experience many difficulties in our realities that we are yet unprepared for. I strongly advise only taking your higher self down as far as your heart chakra until you are confident and used to the crisis that spirit may trigger in your daily reality on the road to transformation.

The higher self is a very interesting higher world being, because it is and it is not everything you experience at the same time. The beauty of the shamanic experience is that divinity expressed as goddess, god or higher self can be experienced as distinct beings that can teach you, bless you, heal you or inform you as desired, and – as you would expect from any connection with divinity – will transform you. Although ultimately spirit guides are made of the collective, they are also individual and unique. One of the particular spirit beings identified with the higher worlds is the *Wise One.* The Wise One at one level is a spirit guide. However, this guide is primarily related to shamanic journeying and the higher worlds. Some people experience the Wise One as an ancestor (near or far), others as a particular archetypal figure (Merlin, Muhammad) and yet others as a bright light. My particular wise one I call Father Michael, I see him as a Christian Catholic monk. This is a relationship I found very difficult at first with my being a witch with a Christian childhood that frankly I experienced as abusive. I now experience Father Michael as a beautiful wise being and we have a deeply rewarding relationship. The Wise One is an integral part of the higher worlds, a being who heals and teaches, a being who reflects to you and aids your spiritual growth.

Lesson Three

JOURNEY TO THE HIGHER WORLDS: MEET YOUR
WISE ONE AND WALK ON THE FAR SIDE OF HEAVEN

Take a deep breath and let it go, relaxing your body as you
go. With each breath feel your body relaxing more deeply.
Feel your head and face relax and exhale. Feel your neck
and shoulders relax and feel the relaxation spread down
your arms, down to your hands and fingers and exhale.
Feel relaxation spreading down the front of your body and
down your back and spine. Spread the relaxation down
through your thighs, down your legs, feet and toes.

On the screen of your mind imagine the number thirteen,
imagine the number thirteen on the screen of your mind.
Imagine the numbers twelve, eleven, ten, nine, drifting
down and down, eight, seven, six, five, down, down, down,
four three, two and one, deep, deep, deep relaxation.

In front of you see the dark brown oak door with a golden
plaque with your name written on it. Open the door now
and pass through the doorway closing the door behind
you. On the screen of your mind see a large meadow with
a tree at its centre. The screen of your mind is merely a veil
between this world and the next. Pass through the veil now.

Walking through the meadow on a late summer's
afternoon, go to the tree at the centre of the field. Summon
your power animals and see them appear next to you. Call
to the spirit of the tree and ask for permission to climb its
branches to the higher worlds.

With your power animals climb the branches of the tree,
up higher and higher to the top of the tree. At the top of
the tree become aware of a staircase made of golden light.
With your power animals, move up the staircase of golden
light until you find yourself pushing against a veil of energy.

Push through the veil and find yourself in a land made

of clouds and dreams. Watch the clouds and dreams float past you. Welcome to the first level of the higher worlds. Continue with your power animals up the staircase of light, up and up until you find yourself pushing against another a veil of energy. Push through the next energy veil and find yourself in a frozen forest with snow on the ground and snow frozen on the trees. Become aware of a white wolf watching you from the distance.

Continue to climb the staircase of golden light with your power animals until you feel yourself pushing against another energetic veil. Push through the veil and find yourself high up on the side of a mountain. Step off the staircase of golden light. To the left of the path, rocks climb higher and higher. To the right of the same mountain path, you find yourself looking out over a beautiful blue ocean hundreds of feet below.

Walk along the mountain path with your power and begin to notice a being of light in human form coming towards you. Feel their wise loving energy permeate your being. Speak to your Wise One, discover their name and listen to what they have to tell you. Your Wise One indicates that you should sit down nearby and places their hands on your head. Light and energy seep from their hands through your body and you hear and feel the healing power of sacred chant.

(Sound, light and energy are passed through the body of the student here).

Your Wise One helps you to stand and helps you with grounding and integration of the new energy. They point out into the sky high over the ocean and with a flick of the wrist light and energy pulsate out of their extended forefinger, creating a horizontal, diagonal tunnel through the clouds. Together with your power animals and Wise

One, fly up through the tunnel of light, deeper and deeper through the clouds, until you fly out of the other end of the tunnel. Below, you see a huge city made completely of divine light. Fly to the far side of the city and land. Welcome to the far side of heaven. Explore heaven and talk to any beings you may come across, divinity, angels or other celestial teachers. I will leave you now to explore and will come back to get you soon.

Thank any beings you are with and fly back to the tunnel of light with your Wise One and your power animals. Fly back down the tunnel of light and land back on the mountain path in level three of my higher world. Thank your Wise One and tell them that a friend of yours will visit soon.

With your power animals, descend the golden staircase of light, push back through the veil and climb back down into the frozen forest, acknowledging the white wolf watching you from a distance. Continue to the next veil and push through into the land of clouds and dreams, down through the next veil and down the staircase of golden light to the top of the tree. Climb down the branches of the tree to the ground. Thank the spirit of the tree, thank and release your power animals and walk back out of the meadow, back through the screen of your mind. See the oak brown with the gold plaque with your name written on it. Open the door, pass through the doorway closing it behind you and climb back up the steps. One, two, three, four, five, feel the energy spinning up through your feet and legs. Six, seven, eight, nine, feel the energy in your body. Ten, eleven, twelve, feel the energy in your head and face. In a minute I will say thirteen and you will open your eyes and remember everything. Thirteen – open your eyes, remember!

Make sure you are completely grounded in the ways described above. The journey that we have just been on is a journey in my higher worlds. Your experience is likely to be entirely different. Indeed, there may be different worlds at different levels. Journey into your higher worlds regularly over the next week with your spirit guides and power animals. Map them and record your journeys in a journal. This recording process is known as the rainbow bridge. It connects the experience of the spirit worlds with the material world. This is something we incorporate in the advanced course and is an experience I greatly encourage, as it really grounds the spirit journey in your body.

After a feedback session, I ask students to split into pairs and journey to each other's higher worlds. At this stage, in the interests of simplicity, I encourage the use of the same route to the higher worlds. The differences in what you experience will be stark, even with this prescriptive way of journeying. Again, go down the steps and pass through the doorway with the name of your partner on it. At the bottom of the tree, summon your power animals and/ or spirit guides and journey to level three of the higher worlds to see your partner's Wise One and listen to what is said. If you choose, you may give a commentary of what you experience as it happens. The student receiving the information is encouraged to "hold space". To do this, imagine two beams of light coming from the back of your heart chakra and moving around to the back of your partner doing the journey for you, holding you both in a protective energetic field. Afterwards, exchange places and journey while your partner receives the experience.

At this stage of the course I teach a technique of clairvoyant reading I learned while training with Kathy Jones in Esoteric Soul Healing, a form of energy healing that updates the work of Alice Bailey, a well-known spiritualist and magician of the early part of the twentieth century. The technique identifies that the throat chakra (the vishuddha chakra) is split into two distinctive parts – the front (that rules external communication, the lower part of the face, the neck and the arms) and the back, known as the alta major, which is where the internal communication (psychic and clairvoyant) information enters the body. I see the alta major located at the top of the spine and base of the neck.

Imagine a beam of light moving from your third eye chakra, to your crown chakra, to your alta major and back to your third eye. Keep the light moving at speed between these three chakras until it becomes three dimensional. Spin the light faster and faster until it becomes a ball of energy. Imagine yourself stepping into that ball of energy and inside you will see a very large cinema screen. On the screen you can see the details of the aura of the person you are reading for. Everything that is happening in their lives is stored as information there.

We close the circle with feedback, prayer and sound/song, thanking and releasing spirit and grounding the magic.

CHAPTER FOUR

THE CIRCLE OF YOUR SOUL: PAST, PRESENT AND FUTURE LIVES

IMOGEN'S PREDICTION that she had kept carefully to herself proved correct. The angry Roman bull did charge again, angrier, more murderous than before, tossing aside all in its path. The dreamers and druids drew their sacred circles and exploded their magic before creating havoc in the ranks of the armies of Rome, raining fire down from the skies and slipping past soldier sentries at night (silently and invisibly) and bringing nightmares to the men of Rome and foreign soldiers of the Empire.

The irony was not overlooked by Imogen. As a magician and a dreamer, she cultivated her relationship with her totem creature of the other worlds. Imogen had flown on the back of her eagle through the mountains of the heavens, across the universe of the middle world and in the fairy kingdoms. She had mastered the art of shape shifting and flew as an eagle with the armies of the tribes. Every time she saw the rows and rows of orderly Roman soldiers they carried the standard of the eagle.

Although Imogen fought now as the leader of the dreamers, and although her magic was as powerful as ever before, her understanding now was different. The universe looked different. The Roman arrow had poisoned her on many levels. The next Roman advance had felt to have been too early for her and her recovery was not complete. The magic that was for healing was used for war. She knew however that time was not her luxury. It was not for her to decide, the grand evolution was in the hands of the Great Spirit, Imogen must play her part in the only way she could understand.

The summons came at the time of Beltane only a few days before the Sabbat. The Grand Council of the Grandmothers and the other tribal elders met at Mona to discuss strategy and consult the oracle. These were indeed extraordinary times! Imogen rode with Jane to the secret location. She did not know beforehand where the council was to be held, only that she would be shown the way. Security was paramount in these times.

Although Imogen had had lovers, both men and women, unlike her mothers before her she had borne no child and she knew that she would not. The decision was not hers, but she suspected she would heartily approve of who the ancestors would appoint as her successor to lead the dreamers when her time came to evolve in the spirit worlds alone. She had known Jane since Jane was a baby, and Imogen had seen Jane in her dreams as her successor many times. Imogen remembered her own initiation as dreamer queen. Elfin, the blind grandmother, had embodied Imogen's dead mother and had crowned her with the great honour of dreamer queen.

When Jane and Imogen arrived, they were shown to a hut in the village compound to dress and prepare. A meeting of the grand council and all of the tribal elders was rare, especially in these troubled times, and was always ritualistic in its nature. Imogen knew that she would be expected to lead the ceremony and oracle for the council. Jane and Imogen, dressed in crimson red robes and corresponding masks, approached the massive tent.

"Who is it that presumes to come into the presence of the lady and the lord?" a voice boomed.

Imogen and Jane could hear that already the drums had reached fever pitch. A bird man stood in front of them barring their entry to the tent. The energy from within was primal, raw and mesmerising. The council and the tribal elders would have been meeting for hours by now; all formal introductions and expressions of lineage complete, all formal strategy and political discussion awaited the embodied presence of divinity. The bird man held a long crystal wand and wore a long hooded black cloak draped over his naked body and his beaked bird mask was complimented by jutting bird like head movements.

"Step aside oh guardian of the gates to the otherworld," Imogen stated as she held his eyes in a challenging manner. "I am she who serves the goddess and the god, I am Danaray the enlightened. This is my sister Calafae being of love. Step aside beloved, you have served the goddess well."

The bird man dutifully, respectively and honourably stepped out of the way and made a sign with his arms of opening an energetic invisible door into the sacred circle. Imogen and Jane confidently entered, feeling the circle being sealed behind them. Women and men from all of the tribes filled the tent but left a space, a circle in the centre, for Imogen to perform the ceremony.

In the east of the tent was a large altar bedecked with figurines of divinity that each tribe served, expertly carved in wood and protected with almond oil. Other artefacts included wands, swords, athames and small cauldrons. Candles, or at least stakes wrapped in cloths of oil, burned on the altar. The council of grandmothers sat each side of the altar and Imogen stood facing them from the centre of the sacred circle.

"Welcome Dreamer Queen," Ertha, the eldest of the grandmothers, said.

"And blessings to you Grand Mother,' Imogen replied.

Imogen took one step forward and raised her voice to invoke the goddess.

"By the powers of the east, the magic that removes adversity, I call on you to hold the space for divinity."

General cries of approval and, "Yes, yes come," filled the tent along with the drum beats.

Imogen turned sunwise to face the south and cried, "By the powers of the south, oh, sacred beings, remove the obstacles to my will so that the Great Spirit can speak through me."

General clamour, drumming and calling supported Imogen's invocation.

Imogen turned sunwise to face the west.

"By the powers of the west, my emotions and my desires and my body I offer to you Great Spirit."

General sounds of approval raucously ensued.

Imogen turned sunwise to the north.

"By the powers of the north, the spirits of my ancestors that bless me daily, be here Great Spirit!"

As Imogen returned to the east, thus completing the sacred circle, the grandmothers and the tribal elders raised the temperature, energy and volume. In her mind, Imogen raised the fire from the core of Mother Earth, span her major chakras out, down and up with the energy and used her breath to expand her aura until it was the size of a number of galaxies. She imaged a holographic, huge version of herself and stepped into her higher self. Expanding her crown chakra, she willed herself to leave her body. Imogen saw herself walking down a long corridor of light. Coming the other way and passing her with a brief nod was her gatekeeper, Arturius, coming to protect her body. His facial expression was resolute and serene.

Imogen found herself standing to the south–east of a large lake which surrounded an island at the centre of which was a large hill which had many of the characteristics of a large breast by virtue of its shape. Imogen felt as if she had been there before, as if somehow she had lived here in a life that she could not recall entirely, but yet she could hear a name, insistent, clear, vivid and silent: "Bereklem". A strange name indeed; reflective, internal and masculine. As Imogen stood beside the lake, a thick white mist of a violet hue descended, obscuring the island and the sacred hill. She heard a sublime musical note vibrating through the mists from the loins of the lake, awakening, or maybe just implying a stirring in her womb. The land of the island appeared to respond with a slight tremble of excitement, a rumble of expectation.

From the left, a black barge began to approach, a grand regal boat draped in long silk black cloth the extremities of which floated in the water. Standing at the centre of the barge was a tall elfin man who seemed to guide the barge effortlessly, telepathically, soundlessly, through the ever growing exciting choppy waters of the lake. The barge pulled alongside Imogen and a ramp was lowered to welcome her.

"Hail Craepo, Elfin Magician Keeper of the Barge," Imogen found herself saying. She was entirely taken by surprise as until that moment she had not felt that she knew him. Furthermore, she knew that he had another name; she felt it just out of reach, just beyond her memory.

"Hail Bereklem friend of the bear," Craepo responded. "Magician returned to us in female form, indeed you are welcome, Imogen of the Oakgrove."

Slightly disorientated, yet effervescent with excitement, Imogen walked up the ramp of the barge, placed her hand in her left pocket pulled out a gold coin and gave it to the elfin ferryman. The ramp withdrew and the barge began to turn and head into the mist, the luscious mists of expectation.

Through the mists, on single sublime notes, she heard a divine baritone voice fill the air.

"I honour who you are."

All sang on the dominant note of B flat major before dropping a whole tone and then climbing three notes and then back to the sublime dominant note to sing:

"Lady of paradise."

Deep in her base chakra, Imogen felt energy begin to stir. More important however was the pulsating ache in her heart.

The divine voice of the god rang out again.

"I see your beauty, maiden of my heart."

As the voice built his love song, the white mist with the violet hue appeared to vibrate with pleasure, the energy built into what could only be described as sexual pleasure. Kundalini stirring in Imogen's spine heightened joy in her mind.

Craepo stood erect in the centre of the barge, arms raised in a V shape, and with a voice that somehow was deeply reverent and confidently commanding he uttered words in a language that haunted Imogen's memory yet remained strange to her. The thick mists parted like the legs of a lover and Imogen saw simultaneously the Sacred Isle of the Goddess and the writhing bodies of the feminine and masculine in their highest form reprinting, refashioning orgasm and mutual ecstasy and returning the divine balance to its primal passionate immanence and transcendence, a complete creative bliss of omnipresence itself. Imogen's kundalini filled her body and mind, and for the first time she understood magic in its entirety.

The barge grounded on the shores of the sacred isle and again the ramp lowered effortlessly and apparently unguided. Thanking Craepo, Imogen stepped off the barge and onto the sacred isle. Energies and memories swept through her body. Again she was consumed by excitement and familiarity; again she knew that she was home. She suddenly became aware of a woman about a hundred metres away sitting on a huge black stallion and watching her intensely. Imogen returned her look and, for a mere micro-second, the woman appeared to shape-shift into a black crow and then, as if it all had been just an illusion, the beautiful dark haired woman was there again, her look exciting, sensual, inviting and intense.

Imogen felt slightly apprehensive and just as she was about to compose herself the woman's face opened into an ecstatic, beautiful smile. So powerful was the effect of her smile that Imogen thought she saw white doves of peace and numerous other small chirping birds singing and flying in the space between them. The woman's arms opened wide in a gesture of welcome, her bright red dress flowed in the breeze and as she sung her welcome her breasts rose slightly and the joy of her melodious voice enlivened all of nature around her. From within the surrounding forests came a beautiful white mare trotting towards Imogen. For a moment, Imogen looked back towards the lake and saw mermaids sitting on the rocks on the banks holding mirrors and combing their abundant hair with ancient wooden cards.

"Come Danaray the enlightened, the goddess awaits you," the woman sang.

"Yes, Thetes, ancient mother of Roodmas, Queen of the May," Imogen replied surprised again at her unfolding memory.

Imogen mounted the white mare and accompanied Morgen Thetes through fluffy white clouds to the sacred temple of the Lady of Avalon on the side of the sacred hill, surrounded as they rode by the singing of the birds.

The ethereal looking temple rested to the south–east of the sacred, breast–like hill. When Imogen looked at it from the outside it felt to be solid, real. However, she couldn't shake off the sense that at different times and in different seasons the temple could just as easily be located elsewhere on the sacred hill. As she arrived at the temple gates with Morgen Thetes, she was challenged by two guardians that although they appeared to briefly and erratically take human-like form were really trees or indeed possibly one tree, or again maybe two trees twisting around each other.

"Bereklem, now Imogen of the Sacred Grove," they said. "Return to us our names. Empower our reality and you may enter the Temple of Avalon."

Stunned, Imogen sat still on her white mare. Gradually, she sensed another being, another time, another life take over her consciousness.

"Stand aside beloved Ents. Stand aside blessed Gog and Magog," she lovingly commanded and the doorway opened.

The temple itself appeared as if it were the land, a grand sublime structure that seemed to be organic and part of the landscape itself, so alive the sense of it was, it felt to Imogen like vibrations of her womb. The Grand Hall of Transformation was by far the most dominant room in the temple and was decorated beautifully and sensually. In the north-west of the hall was a grand throne draped in a violet and gold etheric material that Imogen did not recognise. There were many rooms that were separate yet opened out from the circumference of the main hall. At the centre of the main hall was a large stone well filled with still, clear water. Imogen looked around for Morgen Thetes and for the first time noticed that she was no longer present.

From out of the shadows from eight equidistant places on the outskirts of the great hall stepped eight priestesses, dressed in hooded black robes and wearing the masks of black crows on their hidden faces. Melodic and harmonic voices rang out filling the temple in evocation:

"Um ooh nah, ooh um ooh nah Nolava!"

Again and again the voices called, entreating divinity in her highest form. The vibrations of the voices rang through Imogen's body and filled all the spaces in and around the molecules of the temple. A great light energy engulfed in complete darkness filled the Grand Hall of Transformation. Imogen watched in awe as the goddess began to take shape in black, violet and gold, the Great Mother herself manifesting into physical reality, proud, terrifying, powerful and maternal.

Lovingly, she stepped forward, holding her arms out to Imogen, commanding Imogen to step forward and look into the waters of the stone well. The waters stirred deep in the well causing a number of ripples on the surface. The waters began to clear and an image began to emerge on the surface. Imogen could see herself standing at the centre of the sacred circle in the tent of the grand council and tribal elders. Superimposed around and through her was the violet goddess she had met in the forest before the wounding from the Roman arrow. She could see great antlers extending from her crown supporting the fire of the sun; her aura was made of swirling rainbow colours taking the shape of a tunic around her body. The same voice that sounded of the hills and the valleys rang out through the tent of the grand council of the tribal leaders and, as the voice began to trail away, Imogen felt her consciousness fade into darkness and in that nothingness she no longer experienced awareness.

PSYCHIC DEVELOPMENT COURSE

LESSON FOUR

1. Working with the seven directions, power animals, spirit guides, angels and divinity
2. Journeying to the spirit worlds through your body, the axis mundi/world tree
3. Your DNA, your soul, the circle of your soul's lives: past, present/parallel and future lives
4. Clairvoyant readings and the chakras
5. Grounding and centring.

We teach another form of shamanic journeying, a form that to a greater extent is internal. Access to the inner realms of Spirit involve the practitioner becoming both the journeyer and the portal through which the journeyer passes. So far, the experience of journeying on this course has involved climbing a tree and a staircase of golden light to the higher worlds, or diving deep in a lake and swimming down to the lower worlds. The experience is semi–external and vertical. The more internal journey can be both vertical and horizontal. Via the internal route it is possible to access the lower, middle and higher worlds or to go backwards or forwards through time. We use the scientific idea of the genesis of the universe, the big bang theory alluded to in the introduction. In the beginning the everything was the no-thing and the no-thing exploded/imploded giving birth to itself as the everything expanding itself as infinity. Infinity reaches to the extent of everything it is indeed infinite and yet expanding. Since you the reader, you the student, exist in at least in one reality by definition in one form or another, you came from the no-thing and hence have always existed. Therefore, since everything/the universe is infinite, everywhere is the centre of the universe, your centre is the centre of the divine, the All, the universe.

Many mystic, magical and shamanic traditions refer to the axis mundi at the centre of the universe. Qabalistic and some shamanic traditions see the axis mundi as a tree whose roots are grounded in the lower worlds and whose highest branches reach to the upper worlds while its trunk and lower branches pass through the veil of the middle world. Other traditions refer to the axis mundi as a mountain and Avalonian traditions can see the axis mundi as the Tor, the sacred hill of the goddess. As a priest of Avalon, I work with the Tor as the axis mundi; as a more generic teacher I work with the tree. The myth of the axis mundi at the centre of the universe creates the possibilities of accessing useful archetypes (the mountain, the hill or the tree amongst many others from many spiritual and cultural traditions). When journeying through self to the spirit worlds, you find the axis mundi simultaneously both at the centre of self and the centre of the universe. This placing of self at the centre of everything opens up the potential of the practitioner to journey to anytime or place.

In the introduction we referred to time being a function of physicality. Einstein, a century or so ago, referred to what he called *spacetime,* which he said was curved. That is *time* (the measurement of perception, an energy) being identical to *space* (the measurement of physicality, or ironically the lack of physicality). If the intelligence, the being that was the intelligent energy of the n*othing* (the no–thing) caused itself to manifest as the e*verything*(the big bang and beyond), then at one level the e*verything,* both as *the All* and its constituent parts, must have been present in the *nothing.*

When the *nothing* was the *nothing* and tautologically the *unmanifest everything,* it all existed in this place of *nowhere* or n*ow–here* (as Neale Donald Walsh expresses it in his *Conversations with God*). However the *no-thing* being *everything* at once (or tautologically the *now)* could know itself (as *everything*) but couldn't experience itself *(as everything*). For the nature of experience requires another (time, place, person or thing), which of course there was not/is not, for the divine/universe was/is everything. Hence, through the divine imagination, illusion was created with the function of creating separation. The past, present and future were imagined and the divine experienced/ experiences her/his self. The stories relating to the goddess Madron and the gods Amoun and Narayana describe how they dream reality into existence, meaning that physicality and time do not exist outside their dreams. Paradoxically, because those divine beings are omnipresent and therefore the All, they are not only dreaming time and physicality, they are the embodiment of time and physicality and therefore time and physicality are both simultaneously illusory and real. In my model of reality, this is one of the main reasons why you or I (as divine creators) use the imagination to create the experience of spirit. The imagination is the place where all separation and unity can co-exist. Through engaging with Spirit in the realm of imagination, we are both the transformer of our realities (as the divine dreamer) and the being that is being transformed, because ultimately as divine beings in our unique realities we experience this transformation.

We are therefore made from the divine illusion that we call the physical universe and the mental universe, for who can deny that they come from the universe? For here is the beauty of the divine, the sublime intelligence, the yin and the yang, the goddess and the god, immanence and transcendence, the All expressed through dreamtime. For the divine is both the dreamer and the dream, both beyond the universe yet paradoxically its whole being infinitely encapsulated as the experience of the universe. In the absolute (the divine as the dreamer), all time is now and hence access to all time is possible and logical in the dreamtime we call shamanic journeying.

Because we are made from the universe/the divine, there is nothing about us that is not both the dreamer and the dream. The part of me that is the dreamer, my higher self, my holy guardian angel, the experience of me that is divinity, the All, creates the illusion I call reality through my particular perceptual software I call my lower self (lower selves). My higher self created my soul which in turn created my mind and body to express itself, experience itself, in this illusion of realism. Neale Donald Walsh in his above mentioned work refers to the soul as an acronym:

Singular Outpouring of Universal Life/Love. My soul is my higher self (divinity as me) in a singular form: Spirit is the universal part of that acronym. Since the higher self is divinity expressed as me, and since it creates my soul to express itself in all time (for that is who the higher self is – all time), it is obvious that in my lower selves my bodies in their forms are finite and are experienced in linear time. However as my soul/sole purpose is to express/experience itself in the illusion called *reality* and all time ultimately is now, through shamanic soul work I can capture knowledge and experience from other expressions of my soul (past, future and parallel lives) and bring them into my consciousness to understand myself in a deeper way and thus evolve. That is, as I bring more of what appears to be disparate parts of self (other lives, karma and my unconscious) into consciousness, my evolution, my remembering of my true nature unfolds nearer and nearer to the infinite, sublime, divine consciousness of the All.

There are many techniques, shamanic or otherwise, that successfully enable the student or participant to access past life or future life experience. Some of these techniques that we use on this course of journeying using self as the portal were influenced by the work of Leslie Kenton (*Journey to Freedom*) and many others evolved through years of work. Much magical/ceremonial work creates sacred space in circular form, either ritually in a building, out on the land, or on the astral planes. Many shamanic traditions create a sacred space made of seven directions: north, east, south, west, down, up and self. The seventh place of self identifies the practitioner as the portal for the whole journey. There is an alternative which identifies the energies of the cross quarters. The reason that this particular variation is appropriate here is because the energies of the cross quarters archetypically represent the cycle of time and growth in pagan traditions, and since here we are working with spiritual growth and the illusion of time it appears relevant.

RITUAL, CREATING SACRED SPACE ON THE ASTRAL, THE JOURNEY TO YOUR SOUL IN ALL OF ITS EXPRESSIONS

In this part of the course we look at building sacred space on the astral plane as part of the journey in the inner worlds. Sacred space creates am experience of the raising of spiritual energy, a container for spiritual experience and protection for the practitioner. As a priest of Avalon and a teacher I use parts of the Wheel of Brigitana as a structural approach to the sacred circle, introducing power animals on the wheel and from the lower worlds. We also evoke spirit guides, angels, divinity and other celestial beings from the upper worlds:

Ground and centre yourself in the fires at the core of Mother Earth and the highest star in the heavens bringing together the energies in your heart chakra as you have been shown. Become aware of your heart chakra opening, see the being of light step from your heart and breathe your soul in.

Relax your body down with your breath and your mind and imagine the number thirteen on the screen of your mind, imagine the numbers twelve, eleven, ten, drifting down. Nine, eight, seven, down, down, down. Six, five, four, drifting on down now. Three, two, and one, deep, deep, relaxation. In front of you see the dark brown oak door with your name on it in gold letters. Open the door, pass through the doorway and close the door behind you.

On the screen of your mind see the meadow between

the worlds with the large rock at its centre and the trees all around its circumference. Remember that the screen of your mind is merely a veil between this world and the spirit worlds. Pass through the veil now and place your hands on the trunk of the nearest tree. Feel its bark and its texture. Activate all of your inner senses of smell, taste, touch, hearing, sight and knowing.

Walking through the meadow now on a late summer's afternoon. Feel a breeze on your face and the sun on your back. Feel the long grass under your tread and hear the music of birds and insects as you approach the large rock at the centre of the meadow. When you reach the rock, place your hands upon it, sense its antiquity, its wisdom and its knowledge. With your back to the rock, turn and face the north-east. Silently in your mind repeat after me:

I call to the energies of Imbolc, the energies of healing, alchemy and the promise of spring, the music of poetry and song. I call to the creatures of the other world, the unicorn, the white cow with the red ears and the phoenix. I call to the white swans, the loyal wolves and the snakes of transformation. I call to the ancient priestess of Avalon Morgen Thitis, lady of the snow.

In your mind's eye see the priestess and these creatures coming towards you, when they reach about two metres in front of you, see them stop. Ask them to stay and build your sacred circle. With your back still to the rock turn and face the south-east. Silently in your mind repeat after me:

I call to the energies of Beltane, the energies of divine love and sacred sexuality. I call to the white mare and the black stallion, the doves of peace, the small birds and the mermaids. I call to the ancient priestess of Avalon, Morgen Thetes, Lady of the Clouds.

In your mind's eye see the priestess, birds and other animals coming towards you. When they reach about two metres in front of you, see them stop. Ask them to stay and build your sacred circle. With your back still to the rock turn and face the south-west. Silently in your mind repeat after me:

I call to the energies of Lammas, the energies of abundance and parenthood. I call to the horned and the hoofed ones, the white hind of the other worlds, the cows, the sheep, the goats and the deer. I call to the ancient priestess of Avalon, Morgen Glitonea, Lady of the Heat.

In your mind's eye see the priestess and the horned and hoofed ones coming towards you. When they reach about two metres in front of you, see them stop. Ask them to stay and build your sacred circle. With your back to the rock turn and face the north-east. Silently in your mind repeat after me:

I call to the energies of Samhain, the energies of death and rebirth. I call to the hawk that hovers still in the eye of the storm, I call to the white sow of the other worlds who eats the souls of the dead and gives birth to new life. I call to the frogs and the toads. I call to the ancient priestess of Avalon, Morgen Mazoe, Lady of the Thunder and the Lightning.

In your mind's eye, see the priestess, the hawk, the white sow, the frogs and the toads coming towards you. When they reach about two metres in front of you, see them stop. Ask them to stay and build your sacred circle.

Facing the centre of the circle, with a penetrating gaze, look down into the earth, down to the lower worlds. See your power animals and summon them. See them appear next to you in the sacred circle. With your penetrating gaze, look up into the higher worlds. Summon your spirit guides, the angels, divinity and other celestial beings. See them appear in the sacred circle.

Ask two or three of your spirit guides and/or power animals to journey with you. Explain to them that you are about to do a journey back through time to the circle of your past, parallel and future lives hosted by your soul. Imagine you can dive down your own throat and down into your body. As the darkness clears, experience yourself flying through space with your spirit helpers. Sense stars, planets, moons and asteroids flying past you. Eventually up ahead see a huge black hole sucking matter into its being. Fly now with your spirit helpers to the black hole, sit on its rim and look around you.

Allow yourself to fall backwards into the black hole and. with your spirit helpers. Sense the velvety blackness, the void, the nothingness, the raw potentiality of the no–thing. Feel its endings yet its fertility. Falling, falling in the nothingness, the stillness, down, down into the void. Eventually to your left you notice that the energy feels slightly different. Move towards the energy change and become aware that you are passing through a veil.

With your spirit helpers, come through the veil and find yourself looking at a huge tree, its roots in the lower worlds and its high branches reaching to the higher worlds. Call to the spirit of the tree and ask for permission to pass through the tree and travel back through time. Feel yourself with your spirit helpers pass into the tree and become one with the tree. At once feel a huge force pulling you backwards, backwards through time. Sense yourself as an acorn, back, back, and then as the mother tree, back, back, acorn, tree, acorn, tree, back, back to the original, primal world tree.

With your spirit helpers, step out of the tree. Look around at the primal newly forming universe. Just in front of you see purple bands of light weaving around each other in a huge spiral. Each band of light is of infinite length and one hundred metres across, weaving around in form like a triple helix. Every so often, as the bands of light weave through each other, they form a large knot. With your spirit helpers, fly up one of the bands of light and up ahead of you notice that one of these knots is pulsating. Fly towards the pulsating knot and fly into it. You find yourself flying down a long tunnel made of violet light. Eventually stumbling out of the other end of the light tunnel, you find yourself on the edge of a huge clearing in a forest.

In front of you and your spirit helpers notice hundreds and hundreds of beings sitting in a huge circle. Just in front of you is an old blind person; this is your soul. Move now and sit in the centre of the circle, feel yourself surrounded by all of the past lives you have ever lived, all of the lives that live as who you are now but in parallel universes and all of the lives you will incarnate into in the future. See these beings hold up their hands, palm chakras facing you, sense light from all of their hands coming towards you and divine, sublime sound vibrating through you as you are filled with healing light.

One of your past lives from behind you in the circle stands up and walks towards you. You are taken by the hand and led out of the circle from behind where you were, along a path and back to a life that you have lived before. Go back and observe the events of that life, gather as much information as you can. I will come back to get you soon.

Let your past life lead you back now, back along the path and back to the centre of the circle. From the front of the circle see one of your future lives come towards you, feel them take you by the hand and lead you forwards out of the circle, along a path to a life you have yet to incarnate into. Allow yourself to experience this life. Observe and gather as much information as possible. I will call you back soon.

Let the future life lead you back to your circle of incarnations and your soul. With your spirit helpers, bow to the circle and your soul and tell them that a friend will visit soon and give your permission for messages to be given to your friend for you. Fly back down the tunnel of violet light to the pulsating knot and back down the beam of light with your spirit helpers to the world tree at the beginning of time.

Pass back into the tree with your spirit helpers. Feel a huge force propelling you forwards in time, forward faster and faster, acorn, tree, acorn, tree, forward, forward, faster and faster, acorn, tree, acorn, tree back to the world tree in the time that you entered it. Step out of the tree and thank the spirit of the tree. Step back through the veil and find yourself back in the black hole. With your spirit helpers, muster your energy and fly up and out of the black hole and back through space. Back up your throat and out of your mouth and back into your sacred circle.

Move to the east of the circle. With your forefinger on your dominant hand draw a large doorway of light. Open the doorway and pass through it. Close it and then erase it with your other hand. Walk back through the meadow and back through the screen of your mind. See the dark brown door with your name in gold letters on it. Open the door and pass through the doorway, closing the doorway behind you. Climbing back up the stairs: one, two, three, four, five, feel the energy coming up through your feet and legs. Six, seven, eight, nine, ten, feel the energy in your body. Eleven, twelve, feel the energy in your head and face. In a minute I will say thirteen, you will open your eyes, feel refreshed and grounded and remember everything. Open your eyes, thirteen, remember!"

We instruct students to ground themselves thoroughly and invite feedback from the experience. The students then split into groups of two and journey for each other one at a time. There are six specific instructions:

1.   The student who is not journeying will be in a meditative state. They will imagine beams of light extending out of the back of their heart chakras, circling around their partner on both sides and going into the back of their partner's heart chakra thus creating an energetic protection.

2.   After descending the steps, go through the door with your partner's name in gold letters as before.

3.   Approach your partner's sacred circle. Draw a doorway of light with the forefinger on your dominant hand. Enter the circle erasing the doorway behind you. The beings in your partner's sacred circle may have some information for you or they may not.

4.   Evoke your power animals and/or spirit guides to journey with you. Imagine /visualise your partner and fly down their throat and out into space. The black hole at the centre of the universe is the black hole at the centre of your partner.

5.   Journey as before to the soul of your partner, receiving information, healing etc. Do not attempt to

journey to a past life, or future life, on behalf of your partner.

6.   When you have returned to the sacred circle of your partner between the worlds, draw, pass through and erase the doorway of light as in point three and outlined in the guided journey earlier.

JOURNEY TO CLOSE THE SACRED CIRCLE

Following the feedback of process and experience as opposed to the content of messages in the class circle and any questions that may arise, we perform the following journey to the meadow between the worlds to close the sacred circle:

Close your eyes and see yourself at the top of the flight of stairs. Walk down the stairs thirteen to one. At the bottom of the stairs, see the dark brown oak door with your name in gold letters upon it. Open the door, pass through the doorway closing the door behind you. Pass through the screen of your mind and walk through the meadow to your sacred circle. With the forefinger of your dominant hand draw a huge door of light, enter the circle erasing the door behind you.

Thank and release your spirit guides, the angels, the goddess and the god. See them vanish and appear in the higher worlds. Thank your power animals. See them vanish and reappear in the lower worlds.

With your back to the rock turn and face the north-east. Thank and release the energies of healing, alchemy, music, poetry and song. Thank and release Morgen Thitis, the unicorn, the white cow with the red ears, the phoenix, the swans, wolves and snakes. See them leave and watch them vanish on the north-eastern horizon.

With your back still to the rock, turn and face the south-east. Thank and release the energies of divine love and sacred sexuality. Thank and release Morgen Thetes, the white mare, the black stallion, the doves, small birds and mermaids. Watch them leave and see them vanish on the south-eastern horizon.

Turn and face the south-west. Thank and release the energies of abundance and parenthood. Thank and release Morgen Glitonea, the cows, the sheep, the goats and the deer. Watch them leave and see them vanish on the south-western horizon.

With your back still to the rock, turn and face the north-west. Thank and release the energies of death and rebirth. Thank and release Morgen Mazoe, the hawk, the white sow, the frogs and the toads. Watch them leave and see them vanish on the north-western horizon

Say a prayer of thanks and bless this sacred land, walk back out of the meadow, back through the screen of your mind and back through the door with your name upon it closing it behind you. Come back up the stairs, one to thirteen.

We cannot emphasise enough the importance of grounding, the deeper and more powerful your work the more you will benefit from the experience of alchemy that Mother Earth brings.

CLAIRVOYANT READINGS AND THE CHAKRAS

There is a technique of clairvoyant readings which requires the reader and their spirit guides to focus attention on their client's major chakras. Many of our students already have knowledge about the role of major chakras, so we don't dwell on them in detail. We do, however, outline the roles and functions of these chakras as it aids this particular clairvoyant technique. There are many excellent books written about the major chakras and there are some discrepancies in their descriptions of function and energy, although many of these are semantic and in our opinion unimportant. The Tibetan system, for example, only identifies five major chakras, other systems suggest seven. Whether we see sexuality and money as the function of the root or sacral chakras is more about our value systems rather than one model being preferable.

Chakra	Colour	Physical Function	Energetic function
Root	Red	Bowels and waste material, legs and feet	Connection to Mother Earth, childhood, family ancestory, past lives
Sacral	Orange	Womb (or womb space for men) reproductive organs, kidneys and urinary systems	Creativity, sexuality and money
Solar Plexus	Yellow	Stomach, intestines and digestive system	Seat of emotion and repressed feelings. Often the inner child is found here
Heart	Green/pink	heart, blood and lymphatic systems, lungs and respiration	Unconditional spiritual love, deep romantic love, love for your child

Chakra	Colour	Physical Function	Energetic function
Throat	Blue	throat, mouth, tongue, teeth, arms and hands	1. The front of the chakra – communication, the creative/magical energy of the word, the speaking of truth 2. The alta major (back of the chakra) – the place where the psychic or clairvoyant energies enter the auric systems/bodies.
Ajna	Indigo	eyes, nose, hearing, frontal lobes and pituitary gland	integrating of the personality and the soul. Inner sensing, sight, auditory and kinaesthetic functions.
Crown	Violet/ white/ gold	Head, brain and pineal gland	Connection to the heavens, the great spirit, the All. The integration of the mind to itself and the universal mind.

Please note that the third eye is not the ajna chakra, but in a place outside of time and space. We refer to it as the third eye to avoid confusion.

In pairs, the students take turns to read for each other. The student reading calls to their spirit guides to be present (usually silent in the context of a reading)and begins by focussing their attention on one of the major chakras of their partner, silently asking Spirit for information in any way that it comes: words, pictures, feelings, a cross between or a mixture of those senses. Reading is about receiving and trusting; do not try to analyse or censor. Speak immediately about any information that is received. The more you speak, the more information comes through.

Many students worry at this point that they won't be able to receive anything. It is the worrying, the trying itself, that creates the blocks. Release the trying and breathe. Relax your body and allow yourself to receive. Ask Spirit for the relevant information and tell your client what you receive without questioning them about this information. This is a rule worth working with whilst you are developing your reading skills.

Remember, not every technique is suited to every person. If some techniques work for you and others don't, you haven't failed. I only teach the techniques that work for me, there are plenty that don't and I am a professional clairvoyant. Practice, practice and claim your birthright.

We close the circle with prayer, thanks, releasing, sound, song and grounding.

Chapter Five

Defining Your Life/Soul Path: Mediumship and the Ancestors

WEEKS HAD PASSED since the meeting of the grand council and the tribal elders. Preparations were made and escorts ordered. The Roman Emperor himself had issued orders for the dreamers to be destroyed so much of a threat were they deemed to be. Mogen was tired and drained. She feared the flight from Mona to Avalon as she sensed a personal foreboding on the journey. The Roman armies moved nearer destroying or conquering everything and everyone in their path, an unstoppable force that slaughtered the ram of the Age of Aries.

Imogen had been told of everything that had happened at the grand council that night, the sublime teachings of Nolava regarding the cosmic evolution of the Earth and all of herself expressions: humans, animals, plants, weather and elementals. The Age of Pisces beckoned, the pull of duality and the grand illusion of separation: darkness from light, good from evil, monotheism from polytheism, transcendence from immanence. Indeed, the coming of the Age of Pisces was in so many ways the coming of the Age of Confusion and Plunder, the dominance of the external, the rational, the logical, the illusion as thought forms and philosophy which ironically resulted, Imogen surmised, in the irrational, illogical and ultimately catastrophic.

Imogen had spent many days and nights dreaming, meditating, journeying, gathering information from inside herself and from the mother goddess about the nature of evolution. She had walked the worlds of the faerie and the mountains of heaven, desperately searching for meaning, desperately searching for self. She isolated herself as much as possible in the days before the flight, as she gathered the ancient magic in abundance and sought to soothe her anxiety. The dreamers were to journey with a small escort of fighting women and men along with the very elderly tribal leaders too frail to fight. Boudicca was to launch a counter attack to slow the Roman armies and give the dreamers time. The dreamers would return later to fight a further battle and indeed they would launch magical attacks while they travelled. Paramount however, was the safe guarding of the magic, the sharing of knowledge for the sake of prosperity with the priestesses and priests of Avalon. For Avalon would survive for years to come yet, and its secrets would be kept alive by seers, mystics and the clergy of the earth, albeit through the trials and chaos of the coming Age of Pisces.

For all things move from harmony to disharmony, balance to imbalance, like waves on the great sea of consciousness. The words of Nolava were somehow etched inside Imogen; she was not able to reach all of them yet, they were unfolding in her rational mind bit by bit for Imogen to ponder.

Then like a wave of consciousness it reaches a high point, the life force ignites and the goddess returns in a new age, ushering in thousands of years of peace and the great spiritual leap of humankind with the Age of Aquarius.

For this is the divine story, Imogen knew, a story where an age of humanity was merely the movement of an evolutionary wave, the Age of Pisces merely the winter of consciousness upon the surface of Gaia.

Imogen's astral work involved visiting a being in the middle world she referred to as the "Spirit of Questions". More and more she was becoming aware that the nature of working with spirit and eliciting precise information really required her to ask the correct questions. The spirit of questions had been invaluable in this way: for Imogen this being was male and elfin. With the help of this being she had journeyed to Nolava a number of times searching for ways to appreciate the vast knowledge of the collective spiritual evolution.

The company were due to depart at sunrise the following morning. All arrangements had been made, everything packed and the sentries had returned reporting that the roads and the pathways were clear. Imogen slept early to conserve her strength, and although she had experienced anxiety throughout this period of change she believed she had successfully concealed her worry from those around her. The first hours of her sleep passed peacefully enough. She dreamed of walking the forest alone, dried leaves covering the forest floor, here and there fallen trees or broken branches and twigs. Numerous green plants sprung from the forest floor, birds sang and the occasional doe ran across her path.

In the distance standing in a triangle of trees silhouetted by the setting sun, Imogen saw a large white sow waiting patiently, not moving just waiting. Imogen knew that she must approach the sow in the way you just know in dreams. Bravely in a north-westerly direction she headed towards the sun which she knew would eventually die in the west. As she moved towards the sow it began to transform until eventually standing not far from her she saw Ceridwen the crone, Nolava the dark mother, he had spoken with in Avalon the night of the great ritual of the tribal grandmothers and elders.

"Welcome Bereklem, Imogen, Danaray, child of this dying age," said the great goddess.

"All honour and salutations to you, great mother," Imogen tentatively replied.

"The time has come beloved for you to summon your magic for a higher purpose, oh, Imogen Queen of the Dreamers. As you prophesised as Bereklem, one day you will wear the horns of the ram again with pride."

Memories flashed across Imogen's mind of lives gone past, of Bereklem the friend of the bear willingly sacrificing his life as the great rite led to its logical conclusion and the god king laid down his life for the fertility of the land and the feeding of his people.

"Bring him forth from your being now, Danaray the enlightened. Use your magic to be Bereklem once again," the goddess said.

Imogen reached for the fire at the core of the earth and for the highest star in the heavens. She united their energies at tiphareth in her heart chakra and Danaray, her soul, stepped forth. From the seven directions she summoned her magic, Danaray flickering like an aroused flame. Danaray began to take male form, bearded, stocky, powerful and crowned with ram horns. Imogen breathed deeply inhaling the energy of Danaray/Bereklem into her body. The changes in her body were imperceptible at first, but quickly the sensations increased as her bone and muscle structures altered and coarse hair grew on her face. Her breasts vanished and her sexual organs shifted. She let out a scream which quickly deepened in tone and pitch.

"Welcome Bereklem, ancient king of Mona," the dark goddess declared. "It is time for you to be one with your land again great king. The age is dying awaiting rebirth. Let the hunt begin."

Bereklem bowed to the dark mother and said, "The end of the Age of the Ram is upon us now. I close this chapter with pride, the ancient horns upon my head call for oneness once again with your sacred lands."

The galloping sound of horses' hooves and the sounding of a hunting horn came from the forest. Bereklem ran as an expression of his freedom, his race, his royalty and the last gasp of the age. Through the forest he ran, galloping horses closing in on him until finally he turned to face his pursuers and the dark horned figure of Cernunnos reached down and swept him up easily onto his massive black stallion. The hunt rode and rode, never ceasing its gallop. Thousands of years flashed through Bereklem's mind over and again until he understood the whole experience of the dying age and the ages to come. He saw the journey of the soul and the ecstatic realisation of oneness, the unfolding evolution from imperfection to perfection as the divine became one with all beings again, For the death of the age and the death of the ones to follow flowed in the sea of consciousness ebbing and flowing like the great tides themselves.

The great everything slept and dreamed and raised emanations of itself as divine consciousness in every culture, in every story and in every place, forever showing the greatness and the smallness of itself to itself and adoring its creation. As the hunt bore down on a great archway ahead, Bereklem saw the hag, the crone, the goddess of death herself, barring their way. The horses did not cease or slow, but passed through the very stench of death herself into the summerlands, into paradise. For a moment Danaray heard the weeping of the mother goddess at the death of her lover and knew the lands would rise again, its people with new voices, new journeys, new fantastic possibilities as each age would rise and fall and rise again.

The next morning at sunrise, when the party were due to leave, Imogen was nowhere to be found. Soldiers of the tribes were sent to search for her as those who were left waiting became anxious for news, the leaving party would delay indefinitely – the dreamer queen must be found. Jane paced up and down searching astrally for Imogen, but everything Jane saw was too confusing to interpret. News came at about midday. A tracker had found Imogen's body on the forest floor, a crown of ram's horns on her head and hoof marks of hundreds of giant horses beside her body and through the forest. It was completely unharmed and completely lifeless; it was as if she had just upped and left.

Psychic Development Course

Lesson Five

1. Journeying to the spirit of questions
2. Journeying to the spirit of your project
3. Defining your life/soul's path and working with it
4. Mediumship and asking the ancestors
5. Grounding and centring

Shamanic journeying to experience the spirit worlds is very rewarding and developmental, and if that is far enough for you to go at this time, already you have opened spiritual possibilities which are far reaching and transformational. However, the next stages are more about becoming an equal partner with Spirit, a co-creator, a conscious spiritual being that seeks their own soul evolution on the unflowering growth of holism and perfection. The realisation of this spiritual epitome is well beyond the scope of this course, and indeed this life, for many people.

As the Age of Aquarius rapidly approaches, the inherent urge of many beings is towards the forever unflowering conscious growth of the soul, the massive leap to our next evolutionary dimension. As Mother Earth rotates we experience time, she herself evolves and each sentient being that is gloriously an expression of her evolves too. Many spiritual writers and practitioners focus their attention on the concept that many inhabitants of our planet come from alternative planets, dimensions and original roots. I have no doubt that this is likely, however, the point for us is that all of us in this life and indeed thousands of lives for some have come into physical existence on this planet through the magic and beauty of conception and birth, the very dream of Mother Earth herself, therefore conscious growth with her is appropriate.

Our spiritual evolution is simultaneously both unique and collective, each of us have incarnated to be the greatest, deepest, highest, widest, most sublime expression of who we truly are. It may be true that many of our sisters and brothers (and indeed in many ways, ourselves) remain unconscious of our sole/soul journey. However, the consciousness of it, and the unification with it, is our inheritance, and is at one time or another an inevitability. This though is not entirely our lower self responsibility, for we cannot entirely know why an individual soul chooses to be unconscious in its physical reality. It may be of course part of its greatest expression of itself and its most effective way to heal and balance its karma. For karma is a great blessing indeed – how else can we know that we are the creator of our reality without experiencing the results of our creative expressions?

We do have one great sacred choice though – a choice that chances everything for us and all other sentient beings. We can choose to become conscious and act on our sole/ soul purpose in this life now. We can resolve to recreate ourselves as the greatest, deepest, highest, widest, most sublime expression of who we truly are. This of course is absolutely nothing to do with, or paradoxically everything to do with, anybody or everybody else. For the greatest thing we can do for Mother Earth, all sentient beings that are expressions of Her and all the infinite beings across the entire infinite universe, is to be ourselves fully, consciously, joyously, lustfully, miserably, angrily, powerfully, helplessly in every way possible, which of course is the definition of love itself. Consciously being ourselves leads us to consciously create choices, and those choices lead to the greatest growth, ecstasy etc. Who is it we choose to be now? By making these choices we change ourselves and the collective.

The concept of our life's soul path implies a destiny, a pre-chosen/decided course of action that it is in our interests to follow. We may see this from the point of view of our lower selves as lacking any real free will, for if something is pre-decided the idea of choice is limited. All this of course is only viewing reality from a limited, linear perspective, the external, or separation from All that there is. If again we return to the concept/experience of time, and see it (time) as vertical rather than horizontal, we are able to experience everything from a holistic standpoint of everything happening at once. The present is indeed now, it is a gift and indeed "pre-sent", for reality can be viewed as time both vertically and horizontally and hence the creation story is happening now.

To clarify then, our life/soul path is indeed our destiny,

was indeed mapped at the beginning of time, and it is our free choice in every possible way in every glorious moment of now. Deepak Chopra states that, "The universe isn't only stranger that we think, it is stranger than we can think," and he is accurate. The universe is so amazing, so multi-dimensional that every opposite, every contradiction is united in the magnificent definition of the divine. Finding our life's/soul path is an act of creation, an expression of the divine you cannot fail. It is just a matter of when you choose to claim that knowledge consciously. Conversely, our path is not fixed either. There are always many options and there is never an end point; our paths will always be open, flow, blossom in greater and greater, deeper and deeper ways with more sublime possibilities in the glorious moment of now.

Our life/soul path is inextricably connected to both the experience of time and our tools of creation (thought, word, deed, feeling and belief). Thought/belief as a creative tool allows us to define what in our experience is possible and hence which choices we make and hence how we experience our path. Negative thought (looking away from our greatest expressions of who we are, or seeing ourselves separate from that which we create) slows the experience of time down, positive thought speeds it up. Positive thought can create unwanted effects in two ways: Firstly, thinking only positively can at times narrow our focus and hence reduce the infinite possibilities of choice creation. Secondly, by thinking positively and hence speeding time up we can speed our own growth and transformation to such an extent that Spirit hastens the experience of the clearing of our repressed emotion to such an extent that it becomes too painful (please note, I am not saying *Don't think positively*). There is a third option that usually works for me: "Great spirit, balance this experience for me."

The conscious journey of our soul path is not a passive receiving of information, but is a claiming of heritage, a creative choice at the point of claiming. It is a utilisation of the two most powerful words in the universe, "I am", and a conscious direction of intention. Accessing the imaginative facility central to shamanic work deepens for the practitioner the quality and quantity of their choices in the present moment of now, because it provides a gateway from which Spirit can show greater possibilities. As Imogen realises in the tale at the beginning of this chapter, Spirit answers the question that is asked, and therefore working with the Spirit of Questions broadens the possibilities of deeper, more powerful information being shown.

JOURNEYING TO THE SPIRIT OF QUESTIONS AND THE SPIRIT OF YOUR PROJECT

Ground and centre yourself in the ways we have discussed bringing your soul forth and breathing it into your body. Relax your body down with your breath and your intention. Scan your body for any places of tension and direct your breath to that place for relief. Count down and visualise from thirteen to one. See the dark brown oak door with your name written in gold upon it. Open the door and pass through it, closing it behind you.

See the meadow between the worlds on the screen of your mind. See the ancient rock at its centre and the trees around its circumference. Pass through the screen of your mind and place your hands on one of the trees – activate your inner senses, feel the texture of the tree, hear its leaves rustle, smell its odour in the air and taste whatever it is that you can taste.

Wander through the meadow on a warm summer's

evening. Feel the grass beneath your feet and when you reach the rock place your hands upon it sensing its age, wisdom and ancestry. With your back to the rock, turn and face east. Silently in your mind call to Archangel Raphael, archangel of air. See Raphael coming towards you towards you from the eastern horizon, garbed in yellow and holding a caduceus with two snakes entwined around it. Cross your arms and bow, asking him to stay and build your sacred circle.

With your back still to the rock, turn and face the south. Silently in your mind call to Archangel Michael, archangel of fire. See Michael coming towards you from the southern horizon. His clothes are flaming red and he holds in his right hand a sword of fire. Cross your arms across your heart chakra and bow. Ask him to stay and build your sacred circle.

With your back to the rock, turn and face the west. Silently in your mind call to Archangel Gabriel, archangel of water. See Gabriel coming towards you in a gown of flowing blue holding a chalice at his heart chakra. See him coming from the western horizon. Cross your arms across your heart chakra and bow. Ask him to stay and build your sacred circle.

With your back still to the rock, turn and face the north. Silently in your mind call to Archangel Uriel, archangel of earth. See Uriel coming towards you from the northern horizon, his clothes earthen brown and green. In his arms is a huge cornucopia filled with fruit, vegetables, grains, nuts and grasses. Cross your arms across your heart chakra and bow. Ask him to stay and build your sacred circle.

Facing the rock, look down into the earth with a penetrating stare. See your power animals in the lower worlds. Silently summon them and see them appear next to you in the sacred circle. Now look up into the heavens penetrating the veils, summon your spirit guides, the angelic choirs and divinity. Feel, see and sense these beings appearing within your sacred circle. Standing in the centre of the sacred circle feel the energies of the seven directions: east, south, west, north, up, down and self, centred in your heart, knowing yourself as the portal to the spirit worlds that your fellow travellers will pass through with you.

Identify three or four of your spirit guides, power animals or angels to travel with you. Explain that you are going on a journey to the Spirit of Questions and then onwards to the spirit of your life/soul's purpose. With your spirit helpers, imagine that you can dive down your own throat, down through your body and out into space. See planets, moons, stars and asteroids fly past you. Up ahead you see a giant black hole at its centre. Fly With your spirit helpers to the black hole and sit on its edge looking around at the scene before you.

Allow yourself with your spirit helpers to fall backwards into the black hole, fall down, down, through the velvety blackness, the void, the nothingness. Drift in the peacefulness at the centre of the universe, drift, drift, drift until eventually on your left hand side you notice that the energy is slightly different, a glimpse of light is showing. Move towards this energy now and with your spirit helpers feel yourself pass through the veil.

On the other side of the veil see the huge world tree, the axis mundi, its high branches in the heavens, its roots in the lower worlds. Silently in your mind summon the spirit of the tree and ask for permission to climb its branches to the middle and the higher worlds. Once permission is given, climb up and up until you feel yourself pass through an energy veil. Climb off the tree and down onto a forest path.

Wander along the forest path in a westerly direction, notice the trees and flowers and any animals or birds present separate from your travelling party. In the distance in a clearing notice two spirit beings in human form awaiting you. With your spirit helpers, walk towards them and meet the sorceress and sorcerer of this place. Ask them for the magic to find your spirit of questions and the energy to discover and create your soul/sole purpose. Listen to anything further they may have to say to you.

Note the directions that the sorceress and the sorcerer have given you, thank them and with your spirit helpers follow the path through the woods until you come upon a small wooden hut. Around the back of the hut you find a tall elfin fellow in long brown robes, with a small goatee beard and spectacles. As your party approaches he looks up and smiles as if he has been expecting you:

"I was wondering when you would come, I have been waiting for your return for many a year," he says.

He points to a large wooden easel with a huge piece of chipboard resting upon it. You notice he has carved many questions in many different languages on this board and painted each sentence in a different colour:

"I suppose you will be wanting to know what questions to ask the spirit of your life/soul's purpose," he says. "I knew the day would eventually arrive when you would want to know again."

The spirit of questions studies his board making ahem and tutting sounds for a time, and then he turns and tells you which questions he recommends. Remember what he says, for you will need these questions soon.

"Do you have a specific project you are working on?" he asks you casually.

If you have, tell him and allow him to give you specific questions about that too. Thank him for his time and help and ask him what gift he would like you to bring him in exchange.

Leave the hut of the spirit of questions now and with your spirit helpers fly up and back to the world tree. Continue to climb the branches up and up until you feel yourself passing through another energy veil. You have returned to the land of clouds and dreams in the higher worlds. Continue climbing the tree up and up until you pass through a further veil.

As you arrive in the frozen forest with snow on the ground and ice on the trees, climb down from the world tree with your spirit helpers and this time notice that the white wolf is much closer to the tree waiting for you. Her name is Miriam and she works with Danaray and me. She urges you to follow her. Miriam leads you on a frozen path through the forest until you reach the side of a small mountain and you notice a few hundred feet up a small cottage with a small light flicking in one of its windows.

Miriam and your spirit helpers urge you to climb the steps and to go alone. Climb up the staircase now, up and up to the cottage. Allow yourself to enter knowing that you will be completely welcome. As you enter the cottage, notice its lush décor, and to your left hear the voice of a woman calling to you in one of the side rooms. As you enter the room you see an enchanting beautiful woman sitting at a mahogany desk, a small light burning beside her. Her beauty takes your breath away, and in some part of your distant memory you remember that you do indeed know her. You remember from a place deep inside you that she is a muse. She looks up, smiles and beckons you to sit beside her on a stool. Her voice has a song like quality to it as she begins to speak with you. You may find she sings to you, speaks in poetry or tells you stories. Listen carefully as she answers your questions about your life/soul's path given to you by the spirit of questions.

She invites you to ask any other questions about projects you are working on or indeed anything else. Make a mental note that you will remember anything and everything that she tells you. When she has finished, hear her invite you to return at any time and agree to consult her regularly.

Ask her what gift she would like you to bring her when you return, thank her for her time and wisdom and leave the cottage. Climb back down the stone staircase carved into the side of the mountain, back to Miriam and your spirit helpers and allow Miriam to lead you back through the frozen forest, back to the world tree.

When you get back to the axis mundi, thank Miriam and leave her there in the frozen forest. With your spirit helpers, climb back down the tree, back through the first veil, back into the land of clouds and dreams, back through the next veil and down, down the tree as it passes through the middle world, back down through the veil and back to the place where you arrived at the axis mundi. Thanking the spirit of the tree, pass back through the veil back into the black hole. Summoning all your energy, fly up with your spirit helpers, up out of the black hole and back through space, back out of your mouth and back into the sacred circle in the meadow between the worlds. Give some time to your spirit helpers, listen to what they have to say about your life/soul's path, listen particularly to divinity.

When you are ready, stand at the centre of the sacred circle. Thank and release divinity, the angels and your spirit guides. See them vanish and appear again in the higher worlds. Thank and release your power animals. See them vanish and appear again in the lower worlds. Turn to the north, thank and release Archangel Uriel. Turn to the west, thank and release Archangel Gabriel. Turn to the south, thank and release Archangel Michael and turn to the east, thank and release Archangel Raphael. See the four archangels vanish together.

Walk east back through the meadow between the worlds, back through the screen of your mind and out of non-ordinary reality. See the door with your name in gold letters upon it. Open the door and pass through the doorway, closing the door behind you. Coming back up the steps, one, two, three, four five, feel the energy coming back up through your feet and your legs. Six, seven, eight nine, ten, feel the life energy in your body. Eleven, twelve, feel the energy in your face and your head. In a moment I will say thirteen and you will open your eyes, remember all that has happened and feel aware. Thirteen, open your eyes, remember!

Check to see how you feel, close your eyes and take yourself to the fire at the core of the earth to ground your experience.

A note about the black hole at the centre of yourself: it is an extremely fertile place. An exercise in manifestation that I have often employed has involved planting seeds of my intention in the black hole itself. I imagine I can reduce my intention to seeds made of pure light and plant them or sprinkle them in the black hole for gestation and growth. This may be a powerful exercise in relation to the information that you have been given relating to your life/soul's path and/or a current project that you have. Sometimes, when my journeys have involved some kind of initiatory experience, I have journeyed down the black hole on the entrance to the spirit worlds and returned via a white hole celebrating new energy coming towards ordinary reality. The energy spills and floods through the universe and out into the sacred circle to be blessed, grounded and sent out across the heavens for manifestation and realisation.

We bring our consciousness back to the circle of students and take turns to discuss our experiences. Some students have mentioned never having experienced such trance concentration for such a long period of time and come to realise they are capable of so much more. Most individual experiences are both unique and similar, such is the weaving of Spirit. For those of us who are magically inclined, the sorcerer and sorceress are very useful effective allies.

MEDIUMSHIP

I have an ambiguous relationship with mediumship in the senses of the practice and definition of spiritualism. A recent ancestor, one recognisable to your client, is not necessarily any more evolved than the person receiving the reading. Of course, this kind of mediumship has a very useful and empathetic role to play in relieving grief, but to see it as the highest form of spiritual work is to me questionable. I am grateful however to spiritualism. It has taught me a great deal in relation to technique and I truly believe that many of its practitioners are dedicated to their work with Spirit. However, many are only just aware of their spirit guides, the very beings dedicated to our evolution and to the work we do with Spirit, and many of the practitioners operate entirely in Christian dualism. Their focus is on the top three chakras only and hence many of them are very ungrounded. Often it appears from my observation of many of them in both New Zealand and the UK that their lives are difficult, unhappy and chaotic. The road with spirit is very demanding; it is that mirror of our deepest repressed hurt emotion from this life and others, buried so deeply in our bodies. The techniques of (Christian) spiritualism seem to fall short of the deep personal relationship with Spirit that brings about such great healing.

All that being said, I have met and worked with some full trance mediums who have an incredible relationship with their spirit guides, angels, divinity and other advanced spiritual beings. They work deeply with their own growth, healing and evolution and their work is of absolute surrender to the Great Spirit. My teacher Sally, for example, is one such medium who through her channelling work with Chung Fu has brought direct connection to spirit, empowering and enabling so many people on their paths. I honour her and owe her a great debt of gratitude.

There are three reasons why we introduce basic mediumship techniques in our training: Firstly, for some students it really is their path, at least in the sense of it being their conscious starting point for their path. Secondly, when working full time for spirit, some clients come to resolve deep seated grief issues relating to the loss of a loved one and mediumistic techniques can greatly enhance the process. Thirdly, some of my work (and also some of my teaching in more advanced courses) involves exorcism and space clearing. The ability to connect with recent ancestors has been invaluable in resolving difficulties with lost souls and the process of helping those lost souls find their way home and move onwards on their evolutionary path.

A young woman came to see me a few years ago who had experienced the devastating effects of her long-term partner committing suicide. Working with her helped her to resolve many things and move on in a new relationship. She became one of my students for a time and was remarkably gifted.

MEDIUMSHIP — CLASS ACTIVITY

The students in the circle split into pairs. The reader silently asks for recognisable ancestors to come forward and communicate with their client. The student doing the reading then imagines running up ten steps of golden light and through a door into a meadow. Often there is a deceased friend or family member already waiting for them in the meadow. If not, the reader sends out a mental call for someone to come forward. Many students report it taking some time for the relative or friend to approach them as if rapport needs to be established, I think that this is often a reflection of the personal ambiguity of the students themselves. Working with spirit guides appears to be more ethereal to some students. However, working with people who have relatively recently died seems to create some fear. It is to do with the personal path students take to mediumship; some are indifferent to it and others deeply dislike it. When you become adept at working with spirit, particularly if there is a deep personal relationship with your spirit guides, just asking for an ancestor is usually enough. Sometimes, very ancient ancestors appear which the person receiving the reading has no chance of recognising because the ancestor died in 1326 or at some such date. In that case, thank the ancestor and imagine you have a large pencil eraser. Erase that ancestor's form and send out a mental call for a recognisable ancestor, one who knew the recipient when they were alive. Occasionally, a particular ancestor is out of reach. They appear to go through some process of personal healing that seems to cause them to be unreachable for a period of time. In those cases, the deceased's spirit guides usually approach to give the information and answer any questions that can relieve grief and suffering.

If you are unsure of a spirit being that approaches, challenge them. It seems that asking them a question three times guarantees a truthful answer as to their identity. Alternatively, asking your spirit guides about the being's identity will resolve any doubts immediately. If you are talking to an ancestor and they appear to be having problems staying in focus, imagine yourself running up a flight of stairs of golden light. In other words, raise your vibration and you will find communication much easier. Sometimes when lesser evolved entities approach you pretending to be an ancestor, or indeed a spirit guide, it is worth questioning them to see what their motives are for being present. Often they are confused or lost and require assistance getting home to divinity. Because all time is now, a being can be both reincarnated into another life and still be in the spirit worlds in the form they were before their death.

We close the circle in the usual way with prayer, releasing spirit and song. Blessings and peace.

CHAPTER SIX

JOURNEYING IN THE MIDDLE WORLD: HEALING IN THE ANCIENT TEMPLE OF AVALON

CLAIRVOYANT READINGS

T HE USUAL RITUAL PREPARATIONS and intense meditation preceding the naming and crowning of the dreamer queen had to be suspended for the times were too dangerous to be without a dreamer queen for any length of time. Under normal circumstances, a respectable time of grieving for the loss of the deceased, celebration of her life and a wait for the alignment of the heavenly bodies was required before the new dreamer queen would be named and crowned and the old one cremated. The armies of Rome however were too close on this occasion to afford the luxury of traditional normality and time to reflect. There was a further problem of balance with the circle of dreamers – normally there were nine of them, one for each direction and cross-quarter and the dreamer queen to hold the entirety of the energy. With Imogen gone and Jane suspended awaiting her crowning, there were only seven leaderless dreamers, energetically unbalanced and unprepared for the magic that must be wielded.

Ertha performed a candle vigil in her hut and called on the spirits of her ancestors for guidance, as the eldest grandmother of the tribes the responsibility fell to her to decide the emergency course of action. She meditated, evoked and prayed all night for vision, communication and instruction. The next morning at sunrise she emerged from her hut and called together the tribal elders and the remaining dreamers in conference,

Ertha told of her journeys with the ancestors and the remarkable fate of Imogen. She spoke of the death of King Bereklem of Mona and the end of the Age of Aries. All present were transfixed as if in semi-trance themselves, Jane was both amazed and subdued wondering what powers given could teach her to serve the land and her people as Imogen had.

Ertha spoke of the coming of a new dreamer, a priestess of Avalon and that in the meantime Ertha herself was to hold a dual role of dreamer and elder, also leading the ritual crowning of the new dreamer queen. There appeared to be some discomfort in the conference regarding not observing usual protocol in regards to grieving and appropriate planetary alignment. However, the issue that was of most concern was that the crowning ceremony was to be done in the forest, on the road, and not in the safety of the ancestral haunts of the tribal village. By necessity it would also exclude the other tribes that the dreamer queen served.

Two days after the conference, the dreamers and their entourage were ready again to journey to Avalon; supplies were packed and horses gathered. Imogen's body was washed and embalmed in the traditional way with herbs and a great deal of magic. She was to be carried on the journey and cremated as part of the great crowning ceremony of the new dreamer queen and invoked to play an active role in the passing of the secrets to Jane.The journey to Avalon took three weeks and one day; the party rode for up to ten, eleven hours a day and then took a meal before sleeping. Each time, Ertha had decided that the tribe would perform the passing rites of the dreamer queen things would happen to frustrate her plans. On one occasion, Roman scouts were seen and killed by tribal scouts. On another, an unknown tribe were seen from the party's hill top camp wearing antlers and performing some sacrificial ritual, and on many nights the skies opened and the rains poured drenching people and animals alike as is so common in that part of the world around Litha.

Three weeks felt to be an age, ironically, and concerns about preserving Imogen's body grew. It was rewashed regularly with herbs and perfume and required much magic to keep it intact, however unspoken concern grew daily. Jane found the wait intolerable. She was neither one thing or another, neither dreamer or dreamer queen, Jane felt as if she were in the bardo, awaiting rebirth – ironically of course the rebirth would be at Litha and not Yule, the very mirror opposite. She was to be reborn when the sun was at its height just before the solar god began his descent to the underworld.

Two days before the party arrived on the shores of Avalon, the breast of the great mother and her extended leg could be seen in the landscape of the hills reaching out to the western sea. The travellers rode towards

Avalon with renewed vigour from the north-west; the very sight of the island of the goddess seemed to give them hope and energy. Jane, however, experienced this time differently. She mourned her twin soul Imogen deeply and felt quite unprepared for the initiatory challenges that lay ahead. Her mindset was negative and frustrated; she longed for her home, normality and for this chalice to pass her by. The nearer the travellers came to Avalon, the more the great mother appeared in Jane's mind speaking to her of things to come, both initiatory and in the collective future. For the last few days, Jane had been blocking the voice and vision of the goddess from her mind. However, the nearer she came to Avalon, the more impossible that task became.

Avalon was well protected both physically and psychically; a howling wind and heavy downpour was accompanied by Mazoe's thunder and lightning in the most spectacular of summer storms. As the party neared the boarders of Avalon, the trees emitted energies of fear and panic in their minds and bodies. It took some time before Ertha and Jane could completely steady their senses and hence help the remainder of the travelling party calm themselves. Jane heard the voice of Nolava, goddess of Avalon in her head:

"Speak to the trees, Dreamer Queen elect, tell them who you are."

"I am Calafae of the Dreamers, I am Dreamer Queen elect, we are kith and kin, I bid you let us pass in peace," Jane said silently in her mind.

The fear and panic vanished immediately and completely from the party of travellers. Just as the relief was becoming tangible in the minds' of the party and all were settling, the elven archers appeared in the trees and Morgen Mazoe stood before them, forbidding and blocking their path.

Lightning flashed through the skies followed by loud cracks of thunder. The woman standing in front of the travellers appeared to be a crone in at least her sixth decade of life. However, there was something about her that was much older, much deeper; something ancestral and primal in her aura. A changeling thought Jane, a shape shifter. Jane felt captivated by Mazoe's energy and as Jane felt her eyes briefly closing for a second, she saw a hawk hovering in the eye of a wild storm waiting for the kill.

Jane snapped open her eyes feeling slightly perturbed; the old woman still said nothing. Out of both habit and respect, Jane looked to Ertha to take the lead. Ertha remained still, indicating that the responsibility now belonged to Jane and Jane became aware that the habit of looking to others to lead or initiate change was now forever lost to her. She dismounted and led her white mare towards the shape shifter. She became aware that her mind was still wandering and she sensed her anxiety. As she was attempting to clear her mind, she heard the voice of the older woman in her head:

"Use your training, Dreamer Queen elect. Focus your thoughts and then you will know how to enter Avalon."

Jane focussed her thoughts and felt her magic well up inside. She looked the crone directly in the eyes and held her gaze, not as a challenger, but not in submission either, just as one comfortable with her own magic.

"I am ready ancient mother," Jane stated telepathically. "We all are," she added.

Mazoe turned and extended her right arm behind her. With a wrist movement that was obviously symbolic and magical, yet unknown to any in the party, Mazoe appeared to change the energy of the air around her. It was then they first heard her voice out loud, bird-like, ancient, in a reflective language none of them remembered, but they all felt the stirrings of memory from lives past. A huge wall of mist rose up behind Mazoe, thick and fog–like. From beneath her robes she revealed a small handheld sickle which she used to carve a door in the mist. The door swung open and Jane and the travellers from Mona were able to pass through the doorway freely.

Passing through the doorway brought the party out on the south side of the sacred hill of the goddess. Directly in front of them was an entrance to a great temple which appeared both solid and ethereal simultaneously. Priestesses dressed in violet robes along with various elemental beings appeared to be busily preparing for some upcoming celebrations. Voices could be heard, both male and female, singing, or rather practicing songs which would stop after one line of music and be repeated many times until perfect. No men had been seen by the party up until this point, although the sense and energy of masculinity was present.

A young priestess approached the travellers and exchanged formal greetings with the elders as was proper and honourable. The party could feel however that she was not to be able to keep her eyes away from Jane for any length of time. It was as if she had some kind of foreknowledge of events regarding the dreamers that all others, including Jane, in the party, were unaware of.

"What is your name sister?" Jane enquired.

"I am Morgaine Barjan," the other replied. "You are so welcome here, Dreamer Queen. I have foreseen your coming in the sacred waters for many months."

Jane felt both surprised and completely serene, as if she were expecting such an arrangement. "I am honoured to make your acquaintance, Morgaine Barjan," she said.

The young priestess called for others to help the visitors with their horses, show them to the huts that had been provided and remove Imogen's body to a room at the side of the temple set aside for the honoured dead. An hour or so later Morgaine Barjan came with a message that Jane was to come to the temple into the presence of the goddess. Jane followed the young priestess down the path from the huts to the west of the temple. She asked Morgaine Barjan what ceremony the people were preparing for, wondering at the same time whether Avalonian ceremonies were similar to those of Mona. Jane was stunned by the answer.

"The king of the age has sacrificed himself for the land. We prepare for Litha and the crowning of the dreamer queen. What you see here is a culmination of many months work," replied the priestess.

"So you knew that Imogen would die and I would be crowned dreamer queen here in Avalon many months ago?" Jane stammered.

"Yes I saw it all at Ostara," Morgaine Barjan replied.

They walked on in silence for a short while and then Morgaine Barjan said, "You may find that Litha is slightly different to Avalon."

"Oh, and why?" Jane responded.

"It is a water festival here; it is the song of the land," said the priestess.

When Morgaine Barjan and Jane arrived at the temple, the immediate vicinity around the temple and inside the Great Hall of Transformation was deserted. Jane looked around amazed – it was as if the temple building blocks were a natural part of the land itself, organic, living in every way. Energetically, Jane could feel the guardians of the temple on the astral plane. However, she didn't evoke them and they did not come. She was also aware of a collective spirit of the temple, and indeed the sacred isle itself, a being made of collective thought forms, independent on many levels but not divinity. The being felt to be watching Jane intensely. She felt no hostility from it, only fascination. Jane knew that Morgaine Barjan was entirely aware of these beings, so psychic was her demeanour, yet she, Morgaine Barjan, said nothing.

Jane observed Morgaine Barjan, watching her subtly. It was as if somehow Jane knew her, although they had only met that day. Morgaine Barjan was very young, almost a child, yet Jane saw something womanly, mature and powerful in her psychic intensity, a seer's ability much stronger than Jane had experienced before. Morgaine Barjan became aware that she was being scrutinised, such a sensitive being she was. She sensed deep affection though from the warmth of Jane's personality and also from some deeper level of connection. She, Morgaine Barjan, also held a deep regard, an awe of Jane. The work of the dreamer queen was famed throughout the land and she knew that spirit had made the right choice regarding Imogen's successor.

"As a priestess of Avalon," said Jane to Morgaine Barjan, "do you personally have a specific role?"

"I am a seer," replied the priestess.

"Yes," said Jane, "however, there is something more, something related … wait, who are the thirty-three?"

"I see, dreamer queen, that your senses are very attuned," said the priestess. "Thirty-three grandmothers, primal beings who hold Gaia's energy work with and through me guiding the development of the age. I have a dual relationship with them; in human form I am their vehicle, however in pure spirit I am one of them. Calm now though, dreamer queen elect, the goddess wishes to speak with you."

Sublime sound filled the temple of the Lady of

Avalon. Morgaine Barjan sang the most beautiful evocation in the deeply reflective language of the sacred lands. She sang of the future and the withdrawal of the sacred isle into the faerie worlds and the mists. Her voice summoned the queen of the fairie, the weaver of the web of time and the structure of the universe. She called on the lady of magic and the deep mysteries of the unmanifested. She sincerely called to the lady of the Holy Grail. Jane found herself slipping deeper and deeper into a trance state. She could feel herself falling in love with the song of evocation to the goddess of paradise, and for the first time she could see herself as dreamer queen in her own right.

Morgaine Barjan appeared to reach an energetic apex and she sang her next stanza. Jane saw Nolava of Paradise beginning to manifest in front of her:

Take my life and melt it down
In the fires of your smithy.
Transform the metals of who I am
To the gold of my soul.

In the centre of the Great Hall of Transformation Jane saw the lady whose antlers hold the sun and whose aura radiates rainbow light. Her voice that thrilled like the morning sun called Jane forth.

"Blessings and peace my dreamer queen, so welcome here is your return to Avalon. As dreamer queen in different lives you have been here twice before, and the magic and the sight are in the very detailed fabric of your body."

"I have been dreamer queen before?" asked Jane in absolute amazement.

"This will be your third incarnation as dreamer queen, beloved," the goddess replied, "and this will be the life of the greatest challenge. How you grieve, my child, how you doubt your deepest love, wisdom and power. Reach inside yourself my dreamer queen, reach into the deepest and darkest places and know we are one."

Light, violet and white, emanated from the eyes, ajna and palms of the goddess filling and surrounding Jane. It was as if the very energy itself vibrated through her skin, her muscle tissue, her organs, blood and bones. Deeper the sound/light/energy vibrations penetrated beyond the barriers of the ego self and out into eternity. Ancient lives and ancestral stories passed through Jane's consciousness. She saw the terrible face of the goddess of death, the joy of the maiden, the love of the mother and the passion of the lover goddess, the cycles of life and the journey of the All.

Through the healing light/sound that shattered all of her walls of resistance and shook all of her illusions of inadequacy Jane heard the voice of Nolava in her mind:

"Dream the new age, beloved. Dream unity as Pisces brings duality. Dream balance to counter dominance. Hold this moment of now alive in your consciousness as it is, through the lines of mystics and witches and the reinvention of my priestesses will I return."

Jane found herself alone in the temple, or so she thought, until she realised she had not completely returned to ordinary reality. Eventually she became aware of Morgaine Barjan standing next to her and holding her hand.

"Two nights," said Morgaine Barjan "must you spend with the body of the last dreamer queen. You shall not, however, be alone for I will be there. Imogen and the ancestral Grandmothers will use my body to speak with you and prepare you for your sacred duties."

Jane nodded her agreement.

PSYCHIC DEVELOPMENT COURSE

LESSON SIX

1. Journeying in the middle worlds
2. Journeying through another person's chakras to the middle worlds
3. Healing in the ancient Temple of Avalon
4. Clairvoyant readings with your spirit guides
5. Grounding and centring

For me, the middle world is the parallel in non–ordinary reality to Mother Earth, it opens up access to anywhere in the universe at any time. It is both manifest and unmanifest simultaneously, the landscape both personal and universal/archetypal. As with the lower and higher worlds, the journey is via intent, and to a certain extent trust and surrender to Spirit, at least initially until you become cognisant with the geography, that is until you have mapped this world for yourself. There are locations, however, in the middle world that are not entirely unique. They are part of the collective psyche and hence hold secrets, power and potential danger. I will not address those places here as many of them are related to magical training and hence outside the scope of this book and by their nature secret.

The middle world holds the promise of initiation. Beings may challenge you and because you meet their challenge, you gain knowledge and future allies. Adversaries become allies here, yet the process of that experience can still be alarming. There are many discarnate beings here in the middle world, beings who do not know they are dead or refuse to acknowledge that eventually they will move towards the light and evolve on their soul/sole path. Much of my exorcism and space clearing work takes part in the middle world, either starting here in this world or indeed having its genesis in the middle world.

My personal journey work with discarnate beings is about empathy and compassion. Usually when asked to clear a building, or indeed a person from a discarnate being presenting problems, I soon became aware that usually this being or beings is/are asking for help. I do not give these beings any choice; they are going to the next stage of life. However, I seek to take them with compassion (usually via the middle world) to a sacred place and aspect of divinity appropriate to their belief and cultural structures. Only if it is not obvious, or that discarnate being has no belief affiliation (or indeed they are a pagan from Avalon), will I take that being to the goddess I serve, Nolava of Paradise of the Isle of the Dead.

Taking these beings to my spiritual home is an absolute

joy, as the lady with the rainbow aura and antlers that hold the sun weaves her magic and mystery of transformation and receives with grace and joy these beings into paradise, into the summerlands to rejuvenate, heal and evolve before rebirth. I take Christians to the Christ in the Garden of Gethsemane and Muslims to Allah in Mecca, Hindus to Kali to free their demons and Buddhists to the Bodhi tree to receive enlightenment from either Tara or Buddha (Lakshmi or Vishnu).

Whilst working in Turkey I was asked to go to a woman's home in the south of the country. She was experiencing major disturbances, particularly at night, that were becoming ever more persistent and intense. The usual bangs and crashes were reported, but also other symptoms like the appearance of a discarnate young man, or rather the top half of a severed discarnate young man, beside the woman's bed at night. Understandably, the woman concerned had been too terrified to stay in her home at night for quite some time.

On arrival at her house, I had a sense that the discarnate being was inextricably connected to the woman herself as opposed to the building. I had permission to walk around the apartment sensing psychically whatever was present. There were a few open portals between this world and the worlds of spirit that I closed and sealed. The largest portal however was in the woman's bedroom and it pulsated like an ugly open wound. It took quite some time with energy, sound and light to close the portal, as well as a powerful pentagram to seal it.

I invoked the Wheel of Brigitana in the bedroom, as energetically this room was the centre of activity, and created a sealed sacred circle to work from. I called in (evoked) the spirit guides, power animals and angel I work with regularly. I sat down then to meditate. I wanted to know who this being (or these beings) was. I was not seeking heartless banishment or some kind of retribution; I knew I was present for the healing and the continued evolution of all beings present, incarnate or discarnate.

I saw the woman, who had asked for my help in another life living in the south of Spain during a time of war. She was a Muslim woman whose husband had left her when her son was a few months old. Her son was now twenty-one years old and the bond between them was powerful and loving. Her son and a few of his friends became involved in the war, and during the fighting her son had been sliced in half with a powerful sword. The woman, understandably, was distraught and the emotional trauma had had two effects. Firstly, the woman would not energetically allow her son to leave her even though he had died. Hence, this being was bound to her. Secondly, she had lost any trust in men, as both the two men she had loved (father and son) had deserted her one way or another. In this life the woman reported never attracting the kind of man she would ideally choose and only emotionally dysfunctional men coming towards her.

The woman herself was inside of my sacred circle and I asked her to agree to release her son from her previous life. I called her son into the sacred circle and he came with the few friends who had accompanied him to war. His friends were also somehow bound to the woman and her son. With my spirit guides and power animals, we connected cords of light to the son and his friends and used my body as a portal to the other worlds. My power animals, spirit guides, the discarnate souls and I flew together down my throat and out into space. We flew to the black hole at the centre of self, the centre of the universe and dropped into the velvety nothingness. Eventually, the veil on the left became apparent and we all passed through it.

Seeking permission from the world tree to climb its branches, we ascended to the middle world. We flew eastwards across the lands and sea to the city of marble and gold, the sacred city of Mecca. As a mystic, as a shaman I called on lives that I had lived as a Sufi or Muslim so I could be in Mecca by right. I called on the mother/ father God whose name in Turkish is genderless. I heard the voice of Allah, which I had heard before:

"Open your aura let me fill you."

I was filled to the brim with divine light and experienced myself as if I was a giant closed pair of gates. Suddenly, I was snapped open as sublime light/love poured from inside me, poured from the abode of the divine, drawing the son and his discarnate friends into the light of paradise. The gates closed and I was whole again. With my spirit guides and power animals, we flew back to the sacred circle and thanked and released the Wheel of Brigitana.

I performed banishing rituals and asked the woman to smudge her home with white sage. I sent rainbow lights around the whole building and surrounded and sealed the outside with a dome of light. With an invisibility ritual, I clouded the outside of the dome of light with grey mist so it would not attract beings experiencing negativity like moths to a flame. Later, I visited the apartment astrally via the middle world, inspecting the sealed portals to ensure they had not been tampered with. Sometimes, sealing the portals is not enough; it is necessary to collapse and banish them. I spent much time grounding the experience.

Working shamanically, it is possible, and sometimes desirable, to walk in both non-ordinary and ordinary reality simultaneously. For me, it is this liminal cross over place that allows communication with all earth life – elementals, dyads (tree spirits) and the spirits of plants and animals. On the edge of woodlands, particularly forests, as it becomes dark at night, the trees collectively emit energy that stimulates fear in humans. This is a deliberate defensive action. Communicating with the chief dryad psychically in the liminal space, the border between the physical and spirit worlds, I say something like:

"I am your brother, we are kith and kin, let me walk in peace."

And I find that the fear energy dissipates and I experience a freedom to walk in the forest at night.

Psychically walking with a foot in both worlds is energetically the same as walking in the middle world. There is no strict dividing line. Much of the experience is crossover and much natural law of non–ordinary reality applies. Many shamanic practitioners work this with medicinal herbs, communicating with the collective spirit of the plant. Much spiritual experience can be gained by walking the land and there is no doubt that nature itself is a primary portal into the spirit worlds, particularly the middle worlds. For me, one of the sublime experiences of journeying the middle world is the ability to experience divinity directly in their own sacred sites. Nolava in the Temple of Avalon, the Buddha and Tara under the Bodhi tree, Isis regenerating Osiris in ancient Egypt, Hekate at the crossroads in ancient Greece, the Christ in the Garden of Gethsemane and Inanna on her descent to the underworld of her sister Erishigal.

Working, journeying and meditating with the ancient divine myths and stories begins a personal unfolding of the mysteries and the magic and is experienced so often in one's life as a parallel in ordinary reality. I have worked this way so often meditating with the Buddha, receiving healing and blessings in the temple of Avalon and riding with the dark lord on the wild hunt to the summerlands for death and rebirth. The middle world also has fabulous launching pads to journey to other planets from, visiting the Pleiades or sitting on the Grand Interplanetary Council on the Dog Star Sirius is very revealing.

JOURNEY IN THE MIDDLE WORLD TO THE PLACES OF THE DIVINE

Ground and centre yourself in the ways we have discussed, bringing your soul forth and breathing it into your body. Relax your body down with your breath and your intention. Scan your body for any places of tension and direct your breath to the place of relief. Count down and visualise from thirteen to one. See the dark brown oak door with your name written in gold upon it. Open the door and pass through the doorway, closing the door behind you.

Passing through the screen of your mind find yourself in the meadow between the worlds. Activate your senses as you walk towards the ancient rock at the meadow's centre on a late afternoon in the dusk. Again, place your hands on the ancient rock sensing its wisdom and its ancestry. Feel yourself grounded in this place. With your back to the ancient rock, turn and face south. Silently in your mind call out:

I call to you ancient priestess of Avalon. I call to you crow priestess, Morgen Gliten, Lady of the Rains. Come ancient one and bring the dragon of water, bring the undines, the sprites, the silkies and the korrigans, the spirits of the Water.

138

Sense Morgen Gliten and these beings coming towards you. When they reach about two metres in front of you see them stop. Ask them to stay and build your sacred circle. With your back to the rock, turn and face west. Silently in your mind evoke:

I call to you ancient priestess of Avalon. I call to you crow priestess, Morgen Moronoe, Lady of the Winds. Come ancient one and bring the earth dragon and the elemental spirits of the earth: the elves, the gnomes, the pixies and the leprechauns.

Sense Morgen Moronoe, Lady of the Winds coming towards you. When she reaches about two metres in front of you, see her stop with her elemental beings. Ask them to stay and build your sacred circle. With your back still to the rock, turn and face north. Silently in your mind call out:

I call to you ancient priestess of Avalon. I call to you crow priestess, Morgen Tyronoe, Lady of the Ice and the Frosts. Come ancient one and bring the dragon of air, and on the winds of spirit bring the air elementals, the sylphs.

Sense Morgen Tyronoe and the other beings coming towards you from the horizon of the north. When they reach about two metres in front of you, see them stop. Ask them to stay and build your sacred circle. With your back still to the rock turn and face east. Silently in your mind evoke:

I call to you ancient priestess of Avalon. I call to you crow priestess, Morgen Cliton, Lady of the Sunshine. Come ancient one and bring the dragon of fire and the elemental fire spirits, the salamanders.

Sense Morgen Cliton coming towards you bringing the dragon and the salamanders from the eastern horizon. When they reach about two metres in front of you, see them stop. Ask them to stay and build your sacred circle.

Facing the centre of the circle look down into the earth with a penetrating gaze, call to your power animals. See them appear next to you in the sacred circle. Looking up into the heavens, evoke your spirit guides and any angels that you may work with. Then silently in your mind evoke:

I call to you ancient priestess of Avalon. I call to you crow priestess, Morgen le Fay. Come lady of the Mists, weaver of the magic and keeper of the mysteries. Bring with you the faerie folk from the heart of Avalon.

Ask two or three of your spirit guides and/or power animals to journey with you on your exploration of the middle world. Imagine you can fly down your own throat and out into space. See planets, stars, moons and asteroids shooting past you as you fly at the speed of light towards the black hole at the centre of the universe. With your spirit helpers, sit on the edge of the black hole and look around the universe. Allow yourself to fall backwards into the velvety blackness, the vacuum, the void that is the black hole at the centre of the universe. With your spirit helpers sit on the edge of the black hole and look around the universe. Allow yourself to fall backwards into the velvety blackness, the vacuum, the void that is the black hole at the centre of the universe, at the centre of you. With your spirit helpers fall, drift in this nothingness, this place of potentiality, this unmanifest stillness of Narayabaya until eventually, on your left, sense that the energy is slightly different, its texture variable. Pass through this energy variation, through this veil, and see the world tree in front of you, its roots embedded deeply in the lower worlds, its high branches, its apex reaching high into the upper worlds.

Evoke the spirit of the world tree and ask for permission to climb its branches to the middle world. Climb up and up the tree until you pass through an energy veil into the middle world. Climb off the tree and walk with your spirit helpers along the forested path westwards. Eventually, you reach the clearing where you met the sorceress and sorcerer before. If they are present, greet them and renew your acquaintance briefly. From this place fly up and with your spirit helpers fly west, moving swiftly back, back through time, west, west, back, back. Back to the planes of Wiltshire, down below you, like an eagle eyeing its potential prey from a great height, notice multiple movement. Swoop down now and land nearby with your spirit helpers. See women and men dressed all in white chanting and emitting energy from their palm chakras and third eye. The energy appears to suspend and slowly manoeuvre huge blocks of stone into a standing circle of stones with equally large blocks of stone resting balanced on two of these standing stones. See, feel, sense and experience the magic and devotion of Stonehenge being built.

Fly up now with your spirit helpers and fly at speed further west until you find yourself flying over a large lake. The lake appears to be lightly covered with a mist that has a violet tinge to it. Below, you see a barge moving effortlessly and silently towards an isle at the centre of the lake. To the west, the lake flows out to the sea, a strip of land reaches out towards the sea like a giant leg and the land itself reaches up in the centre of the isle as a hill that looks like a giant protruding breast. Fly down to the hill to a place on its side where a temple is situated. The temple appears to be built from the land itself as part of a living organism, a community of people, elementals and animals live in, and are part of, the fabric of the temple.

The temple doors are open invitingly. Enter the temple with your spirit helpers and find yourself in the Great Hall of Transformation. In the north-east of the temple, notice a young woman turning a spinning wheel. Although she looks very young, she has an aura about her that is older than the mountains of the earth. She points across to the south–east of the temple. As you turn, you see a beautiful dark haired woman combing her hair with an ancient card, whilst looking into a hand held mirror decorated with shells. For a brief second, you think you see small birds flying around her seemingly finding her beauty irresistible. She looks directly into your eyes, and you feel yourself completely transfixed.

She points across the temple to the south-west. As you turn, you think that the pregnant woman sitting in front of a shuttle and loom is familiar. You have a childlike feeling as if you had just glimpsed your mother. The woman stops her weaving for just a moment, looks up and points across the temple to the north-west. As you turn in that direction, you see an older woman in a black cape. Hanging from her belt is a pair of scissors and a handheld scythe. The temple begins to fill with elementals, priestesses and priests. Sublime voices in worship and invocation fill the temple:

Oh Lady of Avalon,
Creatrix of this sacred land,
Nolava, daughter of Anu,
Apple queen of paradise.

Oh, lady of Avalon,
Your creation goes on and on,
Violet lady of the summerlands,
You are the source and the return.
(Song Composed by Sally Pullinger)

Weaving through the worship, mists of violet begin to gather and take form. Gradually, the great goddess of the rainbow aura, the great transformer whose magic heals all, steps through the mists, her hands clasping the Holy Grail at her heart. She calls you forward and tells you to drink from the grail of nectar, ancient wisdom and bliss. As you drink a deep draught, she places her hands one each side of your crown chakra and violet light streams from her hands through your body, vibrating as it is accompanied by primal sound from deep within the goddess. The hymns of ecstasy fill the great Temple of Avalon as each being connects with the great divine.

Eventually you begin to return from a deep trance state and notice that the temple is empty apart from you and your spirit helpers. Leave the Temple of Avalon and fly up and east across the lands and the seas. Eventually looking down, you see open gardens, greenery, trees and plants. As you land in the Garden of Gethsemane, just ahead of you see the Christ waiting for you. If you choose, go and speak to him and find out what it is he has to say to you. I will leave you for a few moments.

Fly up and across now to the ancient lands of Egypt below you with your spirit helpers. You notice an ancient temple. Fly down and enter the temple. On the temple floor see Isis, goddess of magic, reassembling the parts of her mutilated husband Osiris. With light, sound, energy and deep magic, see the body of Osiris taking its natural

143

healthy form and Isis fashioning a new phallus made of gold.

Leave the temple and fly up and across to India. Under the Bodhi tree see the Buddha in meditation, deep in trance. In the energy of his trance, see the goddess Tarag, standing in spirit form, watching you. Approach the goddess of compassion and listen to what it is she has to say to you. Ask any questions you need. I will leave you for a short while and come and get you soon.

With your spirit helpers, fly up now and fly south–west to the mountains of South America. See the medicine woman looking eastwards to the new day. Join her to welcome the morning and sing the universe alive. Again, I will leave you for a few minutes to sample this experience and will come back soon.

Fly back now, fly back to the forest where you first entered the middle world. Climb back down the world tree and, as you disembark from its branches, thank the spirit of the tree. Pass back through the veil and back into the velvety nothingness of the black hole. Gathering your energy, fly back up the black hole with your spirit helpers, back through the vast energy of space, back up your throat and out of your mouth, returning to your sacred circle.

Thank and release Morgen le Fey, the faerie folk, the angels and your spirit guides. See them vanish and appear again in the higher worlds. Thank your power animals and release them. See them vanish and appear again in the lower worlds. Turning south, thank and release Morgen Gliten, the dragon of water, the undines, sprites, silkies and korrigans. Watch them as they make their way to the southern horizon and vanish. Turning west, thank and release Morgen Maronoe, the dragon of earth, the elves, gnomes, pixies and the leprechauns. Watch them as they make their way to the western horizon and vanish. Turning to the north, thank and release Morgen Tyronoe, the dragon of air and the sylphs. Watch them as they make their way to the northern horizon and vanish. Turning east, thank and release Morgen Cliton, the dragon of fire and the salamanders. Watch them as they make their way to the eastern horizon and vanish.

Walk out of the meadow between the worlds, back through the screen of your mind, back through the door with your name on it in gold letters and back up the steps one, two, three, four, five, six, seven. Feel the energy coming up through your feet and legs and into your body. Eight, nine, ten, eleven, twelve. Feel the energy in your head and face and in a moment I will say thirteen, you will open your eyes remembering everything and feel completely grounded. Thirteen, open your eyes remember!

Ground yourselves anyway; it is really good practice and can save from you many difficulties. At this stage in the circle, we feed back our experiences of our journeys in the middle world and then the students are asked to split into pairs.

INSTRUCTIONS RELATING TO JOURNEYING FOR YOUR PARTNER THROUGH THEIR HEART CHAKRA

We ask one student to journey to an aspect of divinity of the other student's choice via the student who is receiving the reading's heart chakra. This can be done by walking down the steps and passing through the door with your partner's name in gold on it and then passing through the screen of your partner's mind and into the meadow between the worlds with the ancient rock at its centre. Build a sacred circle in the seven directions with animals, archangels, elementals or dragons – it doesn't matter. Call your power animals from the lower worlds and your spirit guides and divinity from the higher worlds and use yourself as the seventh direction.

Choose spirit helpers to journey with you and fly down the throat of your partner and out into space. When you reach the black hole at the centre of the self of your partner, at the centre of the universe, fall backwards into, and drop through, the nothingness, the vacuum. Go past the place where the veil is that would normally lead you to the world tree, and drop down into your partner's heart chakra. Notice that there are many doors in the heart chakra and look for the door with the name of divinity that your partner has requested written upon it. For example, if your partner requested that you speak to Isis, look for the door with Isis written on it. When you open the door it is very likely that you will be in the correct place, if not ask your spirit helpers to take you to where you need to be. When you have completed the purpose of your journey, return the way you came, closing and releasing the sacred beings of your sacred circle in the way you have been shown.

When you are with the appropriate aspect of divinity, you can either remember everything that is said for your partner, or speak aloud to your partner as divinity is speaking to you and relay any questions your partner may have for divinity. It is also possible to vary the style of journeying. Rather than going to the meadow between the worlds, you can build a sacred circle around yourself and your partner in your mind. Then with your focus and intention, you and your spirit helpers can fly directly into your partner's heart chakra from where you are.

146

Remember when you have finished to return the way you have come, thanking and releasing any spirit beings you have been working with. Always ground!

At this stage in the circle, we give feedback again, briefly concentrating on the process rather than the content of the messages. All students will have had the opportunity to journey and receive.

CLAIRVOYANT READINGS WITH YOUR SPIRIT GUIDES

Again work in pairs, one takes the responsibility of the reader, while the other receives the reading. The primary reading rule whilst you are training is: *Ask Spirit, tell your client*. Obviously, this creates a rather over-formalised communication pattern, which can be relaxed when you work more confidently. However, at this stage it is a very useful way of working. As the reader, silently ask your spirit guides to be present whether you can name them or not. Imagine them coming around you. Danaray says to me, "When you are doing readings I am not just buzzing around your ears you know; I am busy." She goes on to tell me that she is lighting fires in the hearts of my clients.

Ask your spirit guides to connect with the spirit guides of your client and ask whatever it is the spirit guides want to say to your client. Sometimes, you will find that your guides talk to you and at other times you will experience the guides of your client speaking to you directly. Speak immediately, whatever comes, even if it is just a feeling, articulate it. Move away from analysing or censoring, trust and let it flow as it will. If you are not "seeing" or "hearing", ask yourself what you feel. Reach with your mind towards your guides.

Most professional clairvoyant readings last for half an hour or an hour. Once the guides have communicated everything that they wish, silently and mentally split your client's life into basic categories. (For example, relationships, work and money, health, education, family and perhaps spiritual path if it feels appropriate.) Then ask spirit to tell you about your client's life in relation to a particular category after which you can move on to another category. Allow your client to ask questions and most of all enjoy the process. Some students worry that they may not be giving correct information. Let me remind you that the content in a training circle is not paramount, the process, experience and learning is what is important at this stage.

We close the circle in the usual way with ceremony, prayer, sound, visualisation and song. I remind students to bring robes or different clothes, masks, veils etc. to the next session and to think about aspects of divinity, sacred beings and/or projects awaiting manifestation to put in the astral temple.

CHAPTER SEVEN

BUILDING THE ASTRAL TEMPLE

J ANE HAD SPOKEN to her twin soul Imogen from beyond the veil through the vehicle of Morgaine Barjan. They had spoken of their lives together and the many lives to come. They had spoken of Jane's return role as dreamer queen and of the many challenges to come for the tribes. Imogen talked of her own initiatory experience and of the King of Mona, whose sacrificed blood regenerated the land, and the ram's horns whose memory had called forth the God. Imogen retold the old stories of the tribes, the central myths of divinity and the circular wheel of the year where the God is sacrificed and reborn and the sun that reaches its height at Litha and then starts its descent to the paradise underworld.

True, it was a time of healing, separation rejoined, the pain and the grief filled with healing balm. There was more however, deeper stories of the mysteries newly remembered by Jane but never forgotten by Calafae. There would be a time at the end of the Age of Pisces where Jane, Morgaine Barjan, Rebecca and Isabella would be incarnate and remember the circle of the nine dreamers with Imogen as the dreamer queen. Jane, in masculine form, would record the memory. Isabella of the dreamers would struggle to remember though; she would be incarnate with the others yet separate from them. Imogen reminded Jane of the secrets of initiation, the symbols, the magic, the sounds, the yantra and the mantra. She talked of the tools and the language of the faerie. Imogen also alluded to the new dreamer who was to become part of the circle of nine, young, vibrant and deeply talented. She, Imogen, stopped short, however, of naming her with a promise that all would become apparent at the crowning ceremony of the new dreamer queen who has returned.

Speaking with Noteme, one of the grandmothers who holds the energy of the planet, was an extremely powerful experience for Jane. Beings who knew her oldest soul name, Seybregancanara, had known her as a soul energy since time was new, were all communicating through Noteme regarding the sacred energy of Mother Earth and the responsibilities of the dreamer queen of this coming time.

The huge fire was lit at the base of the southern side of the sacred hill and the flames roared into the night's sky. Jane was robing and preparing in the priestess room on the side of the temple when she first heard the drums. She knew for sure that the druids and Markseyer had arrived. However, she could hear other rhythms, rhythms of the other tribes that she would serve. Somehow, even with the terrible threat of the times, representatives of each tribe had been summoned and had responded. Through her excitement, Jane could hear other rhythms that she felt were unfamiliar. Ironically however, some part of her recognised these other rhythms like a long lost dream trying to surface. She concluded that these were the sounds of Avalon, the rhythms of the Fae and other elementals.

The rites excluded Jane from Imogen's funeral ritual, as the funeral of Imogen's mother had excluded Imogen as dreamer queen elect. Finally, Imogen's body was carried by priests and elementals to the raging ceremonial fire. The drums, the rhythms, the worship, the sound and the dance honoured Imogen's passing. Passion and frenzy were built and many present had the ability, and chose to use that ability, to astrally journey with Imogen's soul to the loving arms of the goddess as she, Imogen, rested before her next journey through time, space and physicality. In this place of infinite consciousness however, Imogen chose to delay, chose to remain in or nearby the physical plane of Avalon. Instinctively she knew she had one further duty to complete in her existence as Imogen, one duty as Danaray, a contract to fulfil with her twin soul Calafae. The other side of self would continue the honoured role of dreamer queen.

Jane was led blindfold from the temple room she had been meditating in when her escorts had arrived robed and masked. She had not known them and this had led Jane to a sense of anxiety and alienation from the events and her environment. The sound about her was deafening – rhythms and drums, loud chanting voices, horns and metal percussion – the energy too was great. Jane felt as if she were being reborn into another time, another place, a new reality.

She felt her robes being removed and at last her blindfold. Naked, she stood at the entrance to a large labyrinth. Stakes six metres high were burning as huge torches every few steps, parallel on each side of the path she was to walk, snaking their way around the sacred hill of Avalon. For the second time that week Jane found her initiatory path blocked by Morgen Mazoe who stood before her at the doorway to the labyrinth:

"Turn away Woman of the Tribes, this path is not for you," Mazoe stated.

"Mother, I am made of stronger metal than that. I come to claim my crown in all humbleness and reverence," Jane replied.

"And yet I sense fear," Mazoe said, "Surely not the quality of a dreamer queen."

"With all due honour and salutations," said Jane, "fear is not correct, but trepidation or nervousness related to the gravity and importance of this path I will happily own."

"I will offer you one more opportunity to allow this chalice to pass you by," said Mazoe. "'Walk away now."

"I will follow my destiny esteemed mother. I am to be dreamer queen thrice over. In these troubled times I am here to take up the sword of my karmic responsibility. Step aside now esteemed mother. Let not the fear of my death turn me away."

Mazoe moved aside and Jane entered the labyrinth of fire staked out along the path carved out by the ancient ones who brought their dead to this sacred hill many centuries ago. Naked she walked, fire everywhere around her, along the path that took her just below the centre of the sacred hill. Jane sensed that she was walking in two worlds simultaneously. Physical earth was under her feet, yet she knew that she was in a state of trance walking the astral planes in vision and sensory acuity. A little further along the path Jane saw Arturius the spirit guide that she shared with Imogen. He invited her to walk with him along the path that wound around the sacred hill:

"This is a journey of your active intelligence," said Arturius, "Through your holistic will, your spiritual, emotional, mental and physical intelligence, has your soul been incarnated to come here at this point in time and fulfil your destiny. You enter this initiation via your intelligence and are reborn into greater intelligence the other side of your rebirth. This is a quest, dreamer queen elect to the core of yourself and with that knowledge you enter again the physical world. For remember, your active intelligence is not your understanding alone, but is the greater knowledge that comes from spiritual experience."

Up ahead, a luminous hare ran across her path indicating that she was heading to the place where the path circles the base of the sacred hill. Jane climbed down the fire path as it rejoined a lower path at the base of the sacred hill. As she arrived on this lower labyrinth path, Jane saw a red hen sitting on a nest of eggs. The hen stood and walked away in another direction and in the nest Jane could see that one of the eggs had something written on it. She picked it up and read the words written in yellowy-gold writing, "The egg of potentiality!"

"Take it with you," Arturius instructed.

As Jane started to walk the path at the base of the sacred hill, she looked around for Arturius and realised that he had vanished and Jane continued the path alone. She began to feel lost. She was neither orientated to time or space and in her mind as she walked the path she was back in Mona, back in familiarity – she was aware of being in her village. However, much of it looked as if it had been sacked, destroyed and burnt to the ground. The central meeting building was still standing and Jane entered it apparently unseen. The building was filled with elders and tribal leaders and Ertha was addressing them.

"We have made a great error," Ertha said. "The first of its kind in the history of these tribes. I am the oldest grandmother and will bear the brunt of the responsibility; I should have listened to my intuition. Now we are ruined, Rome has over run Mona as well. We were failed by incompetence, inability and nostalgia. When Imogen died, we should have never elected her choice of successor, Jane, Calafae, Duganor wasn't ready and we are destroyed."

Others insisted that Jane was responsible for the decline in fortune, and if it had not been for her incompetence Rome would have never penetrated the dreamers' defences. Jane listened mortified, seemingly immobile, but then the vision, as real as it was, vanished and she found herself again on the labyrinth path at the base of the sacred hill.

A little further along the path Jane came upon a wooden arrow–like sign, pointing in the direction in which she was walking. It had written on it one word:

"Will."

Jane focussed her mind. She knew that she had just experienced illusion manifest from her own fears for in the labyrinth, thought ensures immediate manifestation. A little further on she came across another wooden arrow–like sign post and written upon this one was two words:

"Action. Leadership."

The path appeared to open out into a clearing, and very quickly Jane realised that she had returned to the oak grove. Up ahead in the centre of the grove, she saw the sacred fire burning and the dreamers and the druids dancing in a frenzy and beating drums. Jane saw herself with Markseyer the elf at the centre of the circle and from their hearts and third eyes energy poured into the skies above them taking the shape of a fire dragon which screamed fire down on advancing Roman soldiers.

As quickly as the scene appeared it vanished again and still Jane walked the outer path of the labyrinth. Still the tall fire stakes burnt all around her. She found herself weaving between ordinary and non-ordinary reality. Lost in her thoughts she stumbled slightly and felt a pair of huge hands steady her. Jane looked up surprised and in front of her stood an angel of light and of darkness, finely balanced, elemental in its energy.

"Who are you?" said Jane.

"I am you," the other replied.

The angel placed its right hand over her third eye and she found herself flung back to the beginning of time at the speed of thought. Jane saw herself merged with this angelic elemental being, saw herself arriving as part of Gaia forming and shaping what was to eventually become our home.

"Now look again, dreamer queen," said the angelic elemental being.

Jane saw herself standing in the labyrinth and a line of light moving out from the back of her head, back, back through time to herself as the angelic, elemental being when time was new. She then became aware of a line of light extending from her third eye, tearing through time at the speed of light, through many lives to a place of all knowledge, experience, divinity, realisation ... and then the angelic, elemental being of dark and light had gone too.

Jane found herself climbing to a path that was slightly higher, and felt a tangible shift in the energy field. Still alongside both sides of the path, she saw huge stakes of burning flames which definitely kept her warm in her nakedness. As she walked the land, walked the path of the labyrinth, she felt a huge rush of energy fill her body, tearing up her spine from the fire at the core of Mother Earth. She felt her heart open and an intense love fill her. Jane realised that at this time she could sense no separation between herself and the sacred lands, or indeed no separation between the expressions of the sacred land: animals; plants, trees and other humans. It was then that she realised that this great love in her heart chakra was the great spirit of the land itself; it was Ertha of the soil, Gaia of the planet, Avalonia of the sacred isle of the dead and Brigitana from the days when time was young. She could feel her goddess self and knew the power of the dream, the great power of her focussed sexual energy.

In her dreaming Jane was in forested land, protected by another that somehow was herself and yet separate from her. Jane could hear the sounds of a huge wild animal; an unrefined driving force of nature, a wild destroyer and powerful protector. Through the trees she briefly saw a huge stag watching her before it vanished, noble, free, with a cry that echoed throughout the sacred land. She followed the stag as fast as she could with no real hope of catching it if it did not choose that to be so. Pushing through the trees with no warning she found herself in a clearing, a place she didn't know:

"Dreamer queen," a male voice called.

Jane looked startled and slightly fearful. In front of her only a few metres away stood a tall naked man, bearded with feral eyes and erect. In Jane's perception the man's head and face constantly changed, shifted in a way that bizarrely was not disorientating at all. From human to stag, to human to stag again. It was as if in some ways this being weren't even present, as if he occupied time and space in those liminal places.

Jane stood very still, transfixed, like looking in a mirror at a part of self acknowledged yet different:

"Give me your fears and trepidation, insecurity and depths of denial. Look the god in the eyes, full in the face and know yourself, dreamer queen. Know yourself, great goddess."

And as Jane looked she saw the shape of the horned god change and alter, shift and vibrate. In his place stood the antlered goddess, whose antlers hold the sun, whose skin has a violet hue and whose aura is characterised by rainbow light. Jane's whole being was filled with love and compassion and the energy wrapped her in wisdom beyond measure. For the first time Jane looked at her own reflection and knew without doubt that she was divine.

Jane again found herself climbing to the next path, the path that almost circled the centre of the sacred hill, weaving through the fire stakes completely in love with her initiatory journey, her life both as dreamer and the dreamer queen to be. At first she did not appear to notice the harmonious singing, or should I say that at first she never realised that in the sound something new was taking place.

"Come, dreamer queen. Welcome home beloved." Whispers, excited from everywhere. Again, she was between the trees, again in trance as the beautiful clean river flowed past her and the different shades of light sparkled from its waters. "Come, dreamer queen. Welcome home, beloved." The whispers continued weaving through the harmonies of the ever present song. Yet through the whispers and the harmonies of the song, lyrics began to emerge like twigs of on the trees:

Calling you from beyond the mists of time
Re-imagining the great goddess.
Building a new love and the sacred lands
Come, come, Morgen of the faerie.

And as the lyrics rang out of the waters of the river, a vision became clear and Jane saw the wars of Rome all over the globe and saw the souls that were enslaved. She saw the great tides of patriarchy destroying both women and men, as many who fought for Rome had once been her enemy because their choices were dire. Jane watched as the pendulum swept forward in time and Rome fell and so did her empire. She watched as the pendulum swung further away from Immance, the divine mother, embedding itself deeply within separation, separation of women from men and humankind from the divine.

Horrified, Jane witnessed the future war and violence towards the goddess as the land and the goddess as woman. With fascination she saw the war extend to the destruction of the many parts of the goddess that expressed herself as men. Wars and violence spread out over time, all justified in the name of one god or another, yet through the cries of the separation of souls from the divine. Through the illusion of the morality of *My God why hast thou forsaken me* came too such beauty of creativity, the very energy of the divine source itself expressing the sublime as writing, painting, architecture, music and drama. The divine source itself showing the breadth and beauty of all. Through conflict, the depth and possibilities of harmony were shown. As Jane continued to wander through the fire lit paths of the sacred hill the secrets of divine devotion and its magical logic were revealed, divine connection available throughout the coming ages and the knowledge of magic available for every one of her future lives, bubbling under the surface.

Jane stood at the centre of the labyrinth; one moment she was orientated at this centre, the next she was standing naked near a huge fire in the midst of hundreds of people, the people of the tribes and the folk of Avalon.

Horns were sounded and drums beat out the primal rhythms of old, transporting all present to the deepest experience of their genesis. The elderly form of Ertha approached Jane, yet Jane knew the gait, the facial expressions and the energy belonged to Imogen. The sound and the rhythm ceased and all Jane could hear was the crackling of the fire and the laboured attempts to control their breathing of her audience.

The naked form of Imogen/Ertha stood before her holding a silver chalice, engraved with an intricate beauty that Jane had not seen before, just in front of Imogen's/Ertha's heart chakra as if in prayer.

"Drink deep from the nectar," Imogen said, "And know the wisdom of the ages brought about by the sharing of the watchers."

Jane drank deeply of the honey mead and the bitter sweet herbs and knew the minds of her predecessors as if they were her own. So far back did her memories reach she could hear the voices of the original dreamer queens, the shining ones and the Watchers. No more were the ancient secrets veiled; Jane knew unequivocally who she was. Ertha/Imogen raised her arms aloft in a V shape, and in a voice as powerful as the storms she summoned the north wind to bless the dreamer queen and blow away all negativity with the power of Caer Sidi. The winds disappeared as quickly as they arrived. Ertha/Imogen led Jane to a place a little to the east of the fire and placed a blindfold over her eyes. She was instructed to walk painlessly over burning hot embers and feel the passion of fire fill her being.

As Jane walked she was aware of the heat under her feet but felt no pain, her body was filled with sensuality and erotic power and as the fires of her mind, heart and kundalini became one she felt herself transformed. No longer was she Jane of the tribes, or even merely the dreamer queen. She knew without doubt that she embodied Gaia the great goddess of the land. As the blindfold was removed she saw Markseyer before her naked, erect, wild and feral, and as the passion of the goddess and the god mingled, the sublime great rite fertilised the land of Avalon again. Jane was led back to the fire, and before her stood Morgaine Barjan naked. Her sublime voice reached out in song; the invocation to Nolava of the Sacred Isle of the Dead:

"Oh, Lady of Avalon, creatrix of this sacred land."

The body of Morgaine Barjan transformed her aura wrapped in rainbow light, her skin a violet hue. Jane knelt before her on the sacred land and the goddess placed her left hand upon Jane's head and instructed Jane to ground the energy in the fires at the core of the land. As Jane languished in the core of the earth, deep in the underworlds of Avalon, she heard the still voice of Nolava of the Isle of Apples:

"Take my priestess with you, dreamer queen. May she ever embody the union between Avalon and the dreamers. Teach her well for she will be the last of the dreamer queens."

As the primal sounds of the drums, the horns and the stamping feet of ritual participants reached fever pitch, the tiara crowned Jane, penultimate dreamer queen, and the dreamers were complete again. Imogen allowed her essence to drift and rejoin the All; her work was done, her contract complete.

PSYCHIC DEVELOPMENT COURSE

LESSON SEVEN

1. Building the astral temple
2. The initiation of spirit

"'But there is more than that" I said. "That is only the physical temple; there is also an astral temple which we build in the imagination, and what we build in the imagination is real on its own plane. I shall take you through into that astral temple tonight if all goes well.... Look in the mirror" said I. Our eyes met again. I began temple building.'"

When I first read *Moon Magic,* my experience of magic was very limited. The tradition in which I was/am a priest was focussed on the devotional, and although the ritual and the ceremonial are recognised to be magical, the only transformation of reality that was/is sought is one inside self.

The effect of reading *Moon Magic* was one of planting a seed of realisation, that a constant shrine, an inner temple could be placed on the astral plane and it could be as ecstatic as I chose. I was also aware that at the centre of the temple there could be another place, a place of deep personal connection to the divine, a holy of holies where deep transformation could happen. After much thought and meditation, I began in trance to construct my own temple, a beautiful structure on the land with great stone pillars and a great hall for ceremony, a place where I could connect with the divine and also with aspects of spirit that I know and love. I guarded the temple well, placing a door or gate in each primary direction and asking elemental dragons to stand at each entrance and not allow other energies or spirit beings into the temple without permission, something Chung Fu was very careful to advise.

This was a new and powerful journey for me; an experience that I deeply loved. When I started this process, I was still a student priest and a student of Chung Fu's in his development circle. I was working part time doing readings, healing and teaching, but working full time as a nurse. The mixture of this intense spiritual work, with hindsight, was bound to bring radical transformation which came in dramatic form and I left nursing after fifteen years and started working full time for Spirit. During my time in the astral temple at this stage in my life, spirit began to download detailed instructions regarding year long courses to teach. The more I worked in the astral temple, the more my spirit guides suggested the potential of devotional temples as a teaching tool.

But how? My students, although many had raw psychic energy, were not at the level of meditation and visualisation control to plant that intensity of information. Eventually the answer materialised – build the temple through leading ritual and suggesting visualisation through word and sound. The obvious structure to hold the building of the temple(s) came through my own devotional ceremonial use of the Wheel of Brigitana. By leading ritual, all masked and robed, I could build a temple on the astral plain for and with students for them to experience and also access later at will.

Two areas of participation began to develop through this way of working. Students could either evoke aspects of Spirit or divinity that they would choose to work within their own use of the particular astral temple (this was broad and ranged from the Lady of Avalon, to Allah, the Christ, Isis, spirit guides, power animals or deceased ancestors like grandparents or even more occasionally deceased siblings) or they could place potential energies that they chose to manifest in their lives such as those of health, relationship or work. I checked these ideas with Spirit, and the circles or pantheons of divinity that I work with, particularly with the Avalonian pantheon as that was the structure I would use for this work – all was encouraged and acceptable.

The final class of the introductory course started in the same way as the others with feedback and prayer/ evocation. Previously, the students had been asked to develop some idea of what or who they would choose to be in their personal temple. The temple however would be personal to a particular group as opposed to the individual. The truth was that at this point students usually didn't understand completely what we were doing, although most had some idea of they wanted.

The use of sound vibrations and the opening of one's throat chakra and vibrating energy through the body adds exponentially to the experience and power of the connection to spirit. In the Avalonian tradition, we intuit a reflective language and often I use that language to invoke the goddess of that particular tradition, which also contributes towards the overall experience. We instruct the participants to visualise, to imagine the energies coming forward when others are working with evocation and to open their feelings collectively as Spirit works so powerfully through the emotional body. One of my students reported that when she took part in the ceremony at first she was wondering what the point of it all was and then she said, "And then I saw the angels arriving, I have never experienced anything like it." Visualising the temple coming together and being built and seeing it as a whole plays a powerful role in the whole journey.

Before the ceremony we spend time noting which beings or energy each person wishes to experience in the temple and indeed how they relate to that particular being. For example, some students have wanted to work with the Christ. I therefore ask how they experience the Christ primarily. For some he is a healer, so we place him in the north-east of the temple with the healing energies of the goddess Bridie. Some see him as a father, so we place him in the south-west part of the temple with Madron the mother goddess. We tend to ask each student to identify in turn the beings that they wish to evoke in the temple. Often, the ideas of others will trigger new ideas for students who have already spoken, so sometimes this part of the process can take some time.

At this stage, I ask students to change into masks and robes. Ideally, purification rituals with running water and charged sacred herbs would be warranted and beneficial here, but in practice this is not usually reachable in the large room or hall that has been hired to teach in. We gather masked and robed in the circle facing me and (on the occasions I have had a priestess teaching with me) the priestess standing in the centre. We ground and centre and raise energy with sound.

I am now going to describe an example of a temple building ceremony where I worked throughout the course with a priestess. In this book I will refer to the students with initials to protect their identity and to the priestess as "priestess" for the same reason:

BUILDING THE ASTRAL TEMPLE AND THE INITIATION OF SPIRIT

Priestess: Please turn with me and face the south-west. [Everyone turns sunwise and faces the south-west]. I call to you Madron, great mother of all things, you who from within your womb all life comes. Come great cow goddess, you who sleeps and dreams the universe alive. Come great matriarch of the Avallach, the ancient tribes of Avalon who worshipped the ancient mother of transformation, bring your udders full of the milk of human kindness. Come as Mother Ker, the doe goddess, lady of the corn harvest, you who sacrifices the corn so your people may be fed. Come with your shuttle and loom, you who weaves all life. Great mother of abundance be here! I call to you Morgen Glitonea, ancient priestess of Avalon, Lady of the Heat, come with your creatures: the white hind of the other world; the horned and the hoofed ones, the cows, the sheep, the goats and the deer. Great goddess of Lammas be here!

Student S: I call to the spirits of my parents whom I love so deeply, you whose union and nurture brought me safe passage into this incarnation.

Student DE: I call for the spiritualisation of my work, for my journey with spirit in my new occupation. I also call and pray for the health of my parents, that my journey in this temple sends to them the energy of healing.

Student F: I call too for healing energy for my father whose health is deeply failing. I pray that by working in this temple I can bring peace and healing to him.

All are invited to turn and face the west of the temple.

Steve: I invoke the great energy of the west, great Mother Earth, the provider and protectress, you who manifests our dreams and our creations. I call to you as Brigantia, sacred mother of these ancient isles, Great Spirit of our ancestry. Come as the spirit of the hills and the mountains, vales and the trees, come as Ertha the spirit of the soil and Bambha great goddess of Ireland who was here before the floods. Come Great Spirit of the harvest of the fruits and the grains, the nuts and the seeds, the energy of nourishment of the vegetables and the fruits given birth in your body. Come great Gaia, mother of the equinox where light and dark are balanced and the darkness is on the ascendancy as we move towards the dying of the year. Come with the earth dragons and the elemental beings: the elves, the gnomes, the leprechauns and the pixies. Great mother of the winds ground us all in your love. Great goddess Mabon be here!

Student FR: I call to you great elemental dragon of earth, guide and protect us in this our temple.

Student J: I call to the green man, the wild god of the earth, the protector of animals and guardian of the land, be here and welcome to our temple.

Student D: I evoke you great energy of safety and security, bring love to my home, and safety to my family. Bring fulfilment of the basic necessities of life so we can live in peace, bring this energy to our temple.

All are invited to turn to the north-west of the temple.

Priestess: Great mother of thunder and lightning, bringer of death be here with your scissors and sickle as you cut the bonds of life. Come dark lady of the underworld who makes the veils between this world and the next thinner so we can cross to see and bless the souls of our dead. Come Ceridwen with your cauldron of herbs, vegetables and magic as you stir the nectar to create the perfect being of all knowledge. Come with your hawk that hovers in the eye of the storm and your white sow of the other world that consumes the souls of the dead causing them to reborn and experience new life. I invoke you as Shelia–na–gig, ancient one with the open yoni of transformation, as we return to the womb for gestation and reincarnation. Remind us great mother of the inextricable connection between sex and death. Show us your wheel of life. Heal our grief of the loss of the souls of our dead who rest in your body of the summerlands before crossing the veils into infanthood. Be with us here as you preside over our darkness, as you preside in your wisdom at the death of the year. Great mother crone, toothless and ancient one, be here and bless us with peace in our temple.

Student L: Great mother, bringer of death, I call for you and the dark lord into our temple. I ask that either you take my mother with you out of her pain to rest in peace in the summerlands or bring her healing so she can have quality of life whilst still on the earth. Great mother, dark lord, grace our temple with your presence and your blessings.

Student DN: I call to the spirits of my beloved grandparents who have passed over into the other worlds to be present in your love in our temple. Be here to give your love and receive our healing. May our temple be a portal for you to communicate and share your journey of blessing with us.

Student J: I call to the spirit of the white hawk, my power animal. Bring your energy of freedom and transformation as you hover in the storm waiting to take other creatures on their journeys to the other worlds.

All are invited to turn to the north of the temple.

Steve: I invoke the great mother of the north, the Callieach of winter. Come ancient one eldest of our ancestors, great divine source. Come as bone woman, the stone woman, energy of the stillness of death herself. I call to you great Danu, mother of air, you who gave birth to the new sun at Yule. Come lady of the Bardo where we await rebirth, bring the blessings of the winds of spirit to blow the clutter from our lives and bring clarity to our minds. Come as Arianrhod of Caer Sidi, the crystal palace beyond the north wind. Mother of the fish child Dylan and the unnamed one, you who awaits us at the centre of the labyrinth with your healing and who sends the north wind to freeze away all negativity. Come Tyronoe with the faerie goddesses Anu, Aine and Ana, whose names mean love and abundance. Bring the brides of the air, the dragons of air and the sylphs the great air spirits. Grandmother of air, ancestors and beloved beings of spirit whose love aids our life journeys, be here and bless our temple!

Student FR: I call to the spirit of my power animal the golden eagle, I also invoke Cleopatra my guide in spirit, come dear teaching spirits and honour our temple.

Student D: I invoke the spirits of my grandparents and all my beloved ancestors to bless this temple.

Student F: I call to the old woman of spirit who has guided me since childhood. I call too to the energies of my ancestors, be here in our temple.

Student DN: I too invoke the spirits of my grandparents and all of my ancestors to bless this temple.

All are invited to turn to the north east of the temple.

Priestess: I invoke Bridie in her aspect of the alpha feminine, come great ancestor in your form of the maiden goddess, you who brings the promise of spring as the snowdrops grow through the earth and the lambs are born at Imbolc. Come as Brigid, muse of poetry and song, the language of creation, great healer in the fires of your smithy of alchemy. Welcome goddess who hammers the metals of our personalities to reach the gold of our souls. Come maiden with your joyfulness and playfulness. Bring the creatures of the otherworld: the unicorn, the phoenix and the white cow with the red ears. Bring your wolves, your snakes and the white swans that fly through the mists and the worlds of Avalon. Be here white swan maiden and bless this, our temple.

Student N: I invoke my lower animal the snake. Bring your energy of transformation into our temple as you shed your skins and we grow in spirit.

Student SH: I call to the spirit of Jesus Christ, the great healer come, come here to our temple. I call to the collective energy of childhood its innocence and playfulness. I invoke my spirit guide Michael Angelo and my power animal the tiger, be here and bless this temple.

Student DN: I invoke the spirit of the girl child who has walked with me through my spiritual development. Bring me the energy and healing of self-love and the focus of manifesting my healing work. Be here and bless this our temple.

All are invited to turn and face the east of the temple.

Steve: I invoke the powers of the east, the powers of the mind, the powers of fire. Come great energy of the spring equinox where light and darkness are balanced and the sun is in the ascendant. I call to Artha, the she bear mother of the human race and Eostra the lady of spring and the lady of the greening. I call on that energy of life and hopefulness that Graine of the sun brings lighting our way. Come Morgen Cliton of Avalon with your green woodpecker.

Come with the youthful energy of adolescence and the rising experience of the kundalini. Bring the fires that burn away the old so the new may grow. Walk us through your labyrinth of healing to the centre of ourselves and back out into the world again to manifest our growth. Be here Great Spirit of fire and cleanse and bless our temple.

Student J: I call to Archangel Michael, angel of fire, bless us with your presence in our temple. I call to the spirit of my adolescent son who passed to the other worlds. Be here in our temple and bless us with your vitality. I call to the great god Apollo come with the fires of life, love and passion. Come with the fires of knowledge and creativity.

Student FR: I call to the dragon of fire and the spirits of the salamanders. I invoke the fire of life, the fire of determination and personal power. I call to my power animal the lion, the solar beast that aids my journey. Be here and bless this temple.

Student D: I call to my power animals the black bear and the black cat to support this temple and bless this journey. May we build this place to ever commune and be always for blessings and peace.

All are invited to turn and face the south-east.

Priestess: I invoke the goddess of Beltane, the queen of the May. Bring your gifts of divine love and sacred sexuality. Bring the energies of fertility and sexual freedom that raise the blessed kundalini. I call to Rhiannon who rides her white mare through the mists and the worlds of Avalon. Come naked one who was born on the surf of the wave bless us with your divine love and sexual freedom. I call Bloudewedd, bless us with your magic of procreation and alchemy of love, may we worship the divine in sublime erotic abandonment, fill us with your loving. I call to Nolava the lover and her consort Nodens god of the sea, may we know as we love one another we bless you, come with your mermaids and your doves of peace. Bring your card, your comb and your mirror, you who align all life. Be here great goddess of love and bless this, our temple!

Student D: I invoke the winged horse, my blessed power animal that flies through the worlds and lifts me to the great heights of heaven. Be here in our temple!

Student DN: I invoke Kali as the Lover, the wild one of sacred tantra, may sensuality always dominate consciousness as you place your foot on Shiva's chest forever. Bless this here our temple.

Student FR: I invoke Sylvester my powerful black stallion and spirit helper, bring your ecstasy of the gallop and the freedom of the wild abandonment of your speed. I also call for the spirit of music, may your presence be always in my life and here in our temple as you bless my musical work.

All are invited to turn and face the south of the temple.

Steve: I call to the goddess of the south whose love and compassion flows to all beings. Come you who we must all drink from to live. Come Domnu of the ocean deep, the waters and depths of emotion and devotion. Come goddess who stirs out unconscious and brings that which is deep up for us to heal. I call to Domnu of the raging seas and the falling healing rains, come lady of the babbling brooks, the rapid streams and the refreshing waterfalls. Be here Viviene and Nimue, lady of the lake and goddess of the rivers and the veins and arteries of Mother Earth, the great flow of intelligence. I call to you Nolava of water who brings the blessings of the rain hydrating and purifying all beings. Bless us with your emotional cleansing and the maturity of our feelings that manifests our realities. Great mother of water with your creatures of the deep, come as your water dragon and bless this our temple.

Student D: I call to the spirits of the water, to the great mother of water, bring your blessings of deep love and happiness into our lives and bless us with your peace. Bring your love to our temple.

Student J: I invoke the archangel Gabriel, great power and intelligence of water, bring your blessings of emotion and purification into our temple. Come great archangel Gabriel.

Student FR: I call to the water elementals, the undines and the silkies. I call to the dragon of water to guard our temple.

Student SH: I call to my power animal the whale of the deep, come creature of great intelligence and wisdom. I call to Jesus the Christ, great god of compassion and love. Bless us deeply with self compassion and love for each other. Be here and bless our temple.

Priestess: Please turn and face the centre. I invoke you great Nolava of Avalon with your aura of rainbow light and your skin that emanates a violet hue. Come, queen of the faerie with your beauty of transformation. Bring the energies of death, regeneration, healing and rebirth. Be here lady of the isle of the dead, paradise and the sacred lands. Come goddess of the holy springs and wells. Come Avalonia of the isle of apples, the sacred isle of the goddess. Bring your mists and reveal your mysteries of magic and the experience of weaving time. I call to you keeper of the Holy Grail, the red chalice and the cauldron round. Blessed lady of Avalon with your black cats and black crows, you who transforms our dysfunctions and makes us whole, queen of the stars, Morgen le Fey, be here and bless this our temple!

Student FR: I invoke the hosts of angels and celestial beings to bless our temple. I call to Quan Yin, goddess of compassion and love. Be here in our temple of love, peace and transformation!

At this point we raise energy with sound and we instruct the students to visualise/imagine the temple in its entirety. Whilst they hold their visions deepening the details (colours, shapes and hues), the priestess we are working with (if any) and I hold the energies of the temple spirits and bless and initiate each student. We bless and energise the egregore and place four gates to the temple guarded in the four directions by the elemental dragons and the elemental spirits. We close the temple gates and give thanks to close the ceremony, releasing the spirits and divinity we have worked with. The students are instructed how to open, work with and close the temple. We close the circle and hear any final feedback of the experience of the *Psychic Development Course – An Introduction.*

POSTSCRIPT

THE COURSE THAT this book is based on has evolved over a number of years and is taught in either a one night a week for seven weeks format, as the book demonstrates, or over an intensive weekend. This course has now been taught in Istanbul and Mersin, Turkey, Madrid and Malaga, Spain and in London at *Mysteries* New Age shop in Covent Garden and Stepping Stones in Greenwich. Different parts of this course have also been used in South America, Glastonbury, England and in individual work with a number of different students.

One of the challenges when writing is of course self-belief. Is my work good enough to share with others? Is it original within the framework of the vast amount of spiritual writing and spiritual practice by its very nature will influence the spiritual practitioner, writer, teacher and eternal student of the mysteries? The answer of course is the same answer that I give my students, to work with the great Spirit one must trust and one must know that you will always be challenged on your journey, and the blessed beings we commonly refer to as other people by their nature and the nature of reality itself will mirror you in all that you, think, feel, say, believe and do. Needless to say, I owe a debt of gratitude to the lives and works of so many people whose influences have shaped my unique path and whose lives I live in awe of.

The issue of mixing fiction with nonfiction was challenged in the process of writing this book. It was felt that one should not combine the two, either this was a genre of fiction or a genre of spiritual non–fiction. For me however the division is an illusion. The journey of work for and with Spirit is the process of seeing all as the one. For each genre in reality is an interpretation, a narrative we tell ourselves for the purpose of instruction, growth, transformation and enjoyment. I have spent much time and space in this book already working with the idea of the imagination being the primary creative tool, which is therefore both real and fictional and I don't therefore intend to recapitulate here.

Suffice it to say that common to almost all spiritual traditions is the art of storytelling. From the stories of instruction that Dion Fortune, probably the greatest occultist of the twentieth century, used to open up the minds of her students and others, to the storytelling bardic grades of the druids. From the Vedic stories of Hinduism to the poetry of the Suif Rumi and from the parables of the Christ, to the tales of divinity in ancient Egypt and ancient Greece, fiction has been a central part of communicating the sublime mystery of the universe and of the Great Spirit itself. A need to separate fiction, the creative, the intuitive from so called hard facts and scientific reductionism in my experience leads to a poverty of thought, spirit and the art of the possible.

Postscript

Let us politicise the imagination and open it in the way that expands our definitions of who we really are. Let us honour that really there is no division between that which is Spirit and that which has manifest itself already in the world of physicality. Let us expand our capabilities beyond the rational, or to express in another way, let us look from the rational mind into the unconscious mind so we can see the supraconscious as shown to us by the archetypes of the tarot when the masculine looks to the feminine to see the archangel in the Rider Waite version of the Lovers card. For remember, if we follow the metaphor, by the time we experience the Temperance card both the masculine (the logos) and the feminine (the intuitive) when balanced will see the divine equally.

The last thing I wish to express on the subject is the very notion of there being any fiction in this book at all. Critics of the goddess movement in Glastonbury, Somerset, England say there is no historical evidence of Nolava. I agree totally, but also at the same time, Nolava is very real in the spiritual experience of those of us who are a part of the Orchard of Avalon. Through our spiritual work, our ceremony, our prayer, our meditation, the intuition of her language and the devotion of a collective emerging spiritual path the experience of Nolava is very powerful and transforming in our lives. When I have evoked/invoked Nolava in different parts of the world as part of the process of my teaching with Danaray, the powerful spiritual effects that others have experienced become testament to the power and healing of Nolava, goddess of Avalon.

In a sense, the same can be said of the story of Imogen/ Danaray told here in this book. This story has emerged, granted through my peculiar software of perception, through years of work with Danaray and Chung Fu. It has been an experience of channelling information and also direct conversation with both Chung Fu and Danaray in the body of a teacher of mine who was/is a full trance channel. To dismiss it as fiction misses the point of what it teaches the potential of the shamanic and magical experience and the trance expression of the initiatory journey. I don't make claims to absolute truth and conversely I am not looking to undermine anyone else's concept of truth. For me, one of the presuppositions that shape my experience as a priest of Avalon and a devotee to the path of transformation and magic is that it is necessary that I hold in my mind both sides of a contradiction comfortably and see each aspect as equally valid. Yes, Nolava and the story of Imogen is fiction and yes, both are fact in my experience and that of others.

Still, I have no desire to convert you or change your mind about anything. What I offer here is an opportunity to experience spirit directly using the tools I know well. If walking other paths works better for you, or if you wish to hold on to how you see reality without permitting different experiences to shape or alter that in any way, you are equally blessed. For all paths lead home and may your path be filled with joy and peace.

Love and salutations to all sentient beings

Blessed be,

Steve.

Lesson Six